Within
the
Circle

Also by Rosalind Rinker

The Years That Count
Who Is This Man?
You Can Witness With Confidence
Prayer — Conversing With God
Communicating Love Through Prayer
Praying Together
The Open Heart

Rosalind Rinker

Within the Circle

ZONDERVAN PUBLISHING HOUSE

OF THE ZONDERVAN CORPORATION
GRAND RAPIDS, MICHIGAN 49506

WITHIN THE CIRCLE

© 1973 by Rosalind Rinker

Library of Congress Catalog Card No. 72-83867

Printed in the United States of America

To my father
ROBERT F. RINKER
who gave all six
of us loving security
as we grew up

CONTENTS

Now . . .
you who were once outside . . .
are with us
inside the circle
of God's love . . . .
you belong now
to the household of God
. . . . You are all part
of this building
in which God himself
lives by his Spirit.

Ephesians 2:13, 19, 22,
The New Testament in
Modern English

INTRODUCTION

This is the story of my journey through the wilderness of religious prejudice during which God taught me some basic truths in the Bible. These truths became the foundation upon which my writings and teachings have been based these last fifteen years. It is time for this background material to be shared, because without it I would be living in spiritual poverty.

I am best known by the eight books I have already written on conversational prayer and witnessing. The central theme of them all is God's eternal love for us, our love for one another, and the centrality of Jesus Christ. The power contained in this message has astounded many, including myself.

My journey was a long one, and progress was slow. Plowing through religious, social, and moral

jungles had made me both a captive and a
fugitive. But, thank God, the clearing came! And
light. Enough light to make each day a wonderful
happening. Jesus Christ is the Light of the
World and of my world; and as He becomes more
and more the center of my life, inner spiritual
values take precedence over outward conformity.

I am grateful to my Father for His guiding
hand in every circumstance of my life, especially
for giving me courage to break through
programmed prejudices.

My chief difficulties arose from the interpre-
tation of two doctrinal terms: sanctification
and security, which were known to me as "entire
sanctification" and "eternal security."
Surprisingly enough, they both move toward a
similar goal, yet each maintains a scriptural basis
which is unacceptable to the other. Both these
terms have now been redeemed for me, but I
constantly meet others who are still in confusion.
It is especially to these I write, and also to those
of you who are not acquainted with the terms and
the differences. My hope is that you may understand more clearly God's leading in your own
lives and what it means to be His child forever.

In simple language, my concept of the term
"sanctification" led me to believe it was a crisis
experience, arrived at by seeking and obedience,
which would make me free from sin and able to
love God perfectly. My concept of the "security of
the believer" was that it was false teaching
because it permitted a believer to sin and still
be God's child.

For years I skipped over certain portions of
the Bible. Seemingly contradictory truths

(paradoxes) about the Christian life threw me
back upon my own unreliable feelings. Belief in
God's plan and power to hold me securely and
to keep me cleansed eventually came through
several sources: my own experiences, people I met,
books I read, the study of the Scriptures, and
the practice of prayer.

I understand exactly how the ten-year-old boy
felt who gave me this note in one of my meetings:

"I found Jesus three months ago
and then lost Him. How can I find
Him so I can never lose Him again?"

I gladly taught him what it took me so long
to learn.

This book describes the incidents through
which God corrected those wrong concepts.
In the process, I discovered God's great love for
both saved and unsaved sinners and the amazing
truth about the Atonement of Jesus Christ for
all mankind: to bring us by the plan and purpose
of God into His family and on to maturity —
within the circle of His love.

No one is ever changed unless he wants to be,
and even then he is powerless without God's help.
No truth is found unless it is sought, and God
is the prime mover of both the intellect and the
emotions. One only believes what he wants to
believe — until God moves deeply within his
being. Then suddenly the Bible becomes like a
new book, opening and unfolding all its
hidden treasures.

I believe this is true of all men. Wherever
you are now in your search, God is teaching you in
love, and you can't skip over the milestones or

ignore them completely. God is in them all, and each experience is a stepping stone to the next one.

Someone may ask, Do you still have problems?

Yes, I do. And because I know that growth and perception come through conflict and suffering, I am open to everything. I know I am God's child and want to obey and serve Him, but sometimes I find myself lost on some perfectly legitimate human by-path. Then, through His loving-kindness, the Good Shepherd finds His lamb, gathers her into His arms, and she is at rest — in Him.

I am not my own. I am His. He cares for His own to the very end of time and through all eternity. He is greater than I. He is greater than any power of evil. He holds me in His very hands. What can ever separate me from such a Savior?

My grateful thanks to Bob DeVries, Executive Vice-President of the Book Division at Zondervan, for access to his ear at any time via the telephone. And to all my friends who have listened to me and helped me during these two years of writing, especially Lorrie Carlson and Eunice Harris.

The final decision to publish *Within the Circle* as a spiritual autobiography was not an easy one. I am especially grateful to my editor, Judy Markham, for her encouragement and understanding of the whole subject.

If I do not tell everything there is to tell, please remember no one can tell it all. I have purposely avoided using names whenever possible, for I have many friends on both sides of the doctrinal fence. There are some things better left untold and others which are not yet ready to be told. Often I shall understate the cost to me of the truth as I learned it.

Chapter 1

Very early, there was
that baffling knowledge that
there must be a door — but all
I could find was a blank wall.
    Why does it take so long to
    understand, when I know there
    must be more — so very much more?

                                R.R.

WANTING TO PLEASE GOD

They were waiting for me downstairs.

There must have been thirty or forty of them, judging from the talking and laughter which I could hear. I still had a few moments, a few frightening moments, before I had to go down and face them.

Frightening, because I suddenly realized how different I was from them. At least that was the only reason I could find for my fear. What I had to say was important to me, but I wasn't sure it would be important to them.

I was twenty years old and on my way to China as a foreign missionary. I had been invited by a college professor and his wife who were Christians to speak at a college in North Dakota. They felt my testimony could be helpful to the girls who were staying in the dormitory that summer.

But what did I have in common with those girls besides my age? What bridge could I possibly make? Even the language I used to describe what I was about to do suddenly seemed stilted, didactic, and inadequate.

They lived as young people in their own world, and I didn't. The fear of God had been instilled in me. If I did all the worldly things they did, God would not be pleased with me. He wanted me to be a spiritually surrendered Christian. And more than anything else in the world, I wanted to please God.

However, right then that great desire conflicted with the fear of facing those girls. In my distress I wanted to run away and hide. I needed protection. What to do? Where to go?

Suddenly I found myself inside the tiny clothes closet with the door closed, down on my knees with my face literally on the floor. I had found a hiding place, and there I cried out to God in desperation. I don't think I'll ever forget that moment:

"Lord, I don't even speak their language — they don't speak mine. I want to get through to them, but I don't know how! I want to tell them what it means to follow You. But how? Help me! I'm helpless!"

A quietness came to me after that honest admission, and I went downstairs, faced those college girls, and gave them my testimony. Light refreshments were served then, but everyone (including the speaker!) carefully avoided the subjects of religion and being a missionary.

Afterwards, alone in my room, I thought it all over. I had survived the ordeal, although I didn't remember what I had said; I was so relieved to have it finished. But that wasn't enough.

"Dear God, there must be an approach to girls outside the church. There must be some common ground on which to meet, some subject which would open their hearts to Christ. There must be! There has to be! I'll find it if it takes forever."

Why was I on my way to China as a missionary at only twenty years of age? What was my message, and why did I feel it was incomplete? Why was I so distressed and helpless? How did I feel about myself, and why did I feel that I was so different from others my own age?

These are subjects I have never written about before, but now, because they form the background of spiritual emancipation in many areas, there is freedom to write.

My Mother's Story

To begin the story of my spiritual journey — my discovery of the circle of God's love — I must begin with my mother. Lydia Messerschmidt was one of twelve children born to my grandparents, godly people who had come from the Black Forest region of Germany. My mother was born and raised in Minnesota, and when she was a young woman she went to the Dakota territories as superintendent of the New Rockford public schools. There she met a handsome young lawyer who sang tenor in the local Methodist choir. Robert Franklin Rinker II, from Iowa (second generation from Switzerland), and Lydia Messerschmidt were married in Portland, Oregon, took a honeymoon trip up the Columbia River, and returned to settle in North Dakota and raise a family of six children, of whom I was the eldest. "You were beautiful children," my mother

recalled years later. "We were so proud of you
and so thankful to have you.

"Then one day I stood watching three of you
taking your afternoon naps. You were such
healthy, beautiful children; I was overwhelmed
with love and devotion and amazement that I
was your mother.

"As I stood there thinking how much I loved
you and would do anything for you, it was as
if God spoke to me: *I love you, Lydia, more than
you could love your children.*

"I was only a nominal churchgoer," mother
continued, "and to get a clear message like that
stopped me short. Could God possibly love *me*
that much? More than I loved my children?
Could it be possible?"

She went into an adjoining room, threw
herself on her knees, still overwhelmed by such
love from God, and burst into tears of gratefulness.
During the next three days she thought about
nothing else. She prayed constantly, admitting
and confessing every sin she could think of,
until there came an end to her feeling of
unworthiness. She felt cleansed and loved. She
belonged. She knew Jesus Christ had come
into her heart.

But as days went by, her gratefulness for the
miracle of newness which had come to her seemed
to call for an offering on her part.

"My oldest, Lord, You take her in my place.
I'd go—I would have gone—if only this had
happened before, but so be it now. Take her.
Send her out in Your service in my place."

Finding God's Plan

When I was still a child in Sunday school,
my mother, now a devout Christian and firm

supporter of foreign missions, often told my
friends: "Rosalind is going to be a missionary
when she grows up."

They would turn to me and ask, "Are you
really?" I would shrug my shoulders, trying to pass
it off with, "Who knows?" But in my heart
I wondered.

Then on a June morning when I was fifteen
years old, I heard the question which was to
change my whole life.

That day my mother had insisted on
driving me sixty miles from home to attend a
youth conference where I was exposed to the
salvation teaching which we did not get in our
little home church. And that morning my
mother's prayers began to be answered.

*"Have you ever accepted Jesus Christ as your
personal Savior?"* A stranger sitting beside me
asked the question. My response? Well, yes —
I believed in Jesus. But no — I had never invited
Him into my heart; I had never accepted Him
just like that. Did I want to? Yes, I wanted to.
And I did.

The very next night after my conversion, a
missionary from China was speaking at that same
conference. At the close she invited all those
who would offer their lives to go anywhere God
sent them to come forward for a closing prayer
around the altar. They sang, "I'll go where
You want me to go, dear Lord," and without
hesitation, I went forward.

I can still hear those words ringing in my
ears from that night when I dedicated myself to
God's service:

Anywhere He leads me I can safely go,
Anywhere He leads me in this world below —
Anywhere with Jesus I can safely go.

At that time I thought one must have a special call, so in order that I might not miss it, I determined I would live close to Jesus and love Him with all my heart. His call might come any day, just as His Second Coming might take place any day. Both these subjects filled me with great anticipation and motivation.

Chapter 2

Things are not sinful.
Only human beings may be sinful
or "worldly" . . . it is not what goes
into the man that defiles him. It
is our use of things that determines
their effect on us. It is our response
to events . . . that shapes us.
God is not as concerned that we obey a
code of conduct governing outward things . . .
as He is with the heart.

Elisabeth Elliot
The Liberty of Obedience

PLEASING PEOPLE

Shortly after my conversion experience, there was a split in our church, and my mother and father were in the group that formed a separate congregation which soon joined a new denomination. We were told that this new denomination was "more spiritual" than the old because they followed the Bible quite literally.

Ever since I was a little girl I had wanted to do right as well as to be right; now that I was a Christian, more than anything else I wanted to please God. But to me, pleasing God soon became synonymous with outward conformity: that included being separated from the world, being conformed to the saints (the people in the church), and keeping oneself from backsliding by faithful church attendance and obedience to all the known will of God. Any outward deviations could separate one from God, so consequently any guilt that fastened itself upon us came more from "somebody knowing" than from inner conviction.

The big problem in my fifteen-year-old life was: just what was worldliness?

We were to avoid "the world, the flesh, and the devil," but how far could one go in avoiding the ideas, fashions, and practices of this world? The church elders had decided this whole uncertain question for us, and since they equated pleasing God with outward conformity, what could I do but go along with it.

When we joined the church, we had to sign a pledge (and follow it even before we became members) that we would abstain from all worldly lusts and questionable pleasures as listed in the church manual: smoking, playing cards, drinking, dancing, and attending movies (this was long before television came along to make up for lost time).

To interpret this pledge correctly, it also meant that whatever was in fashion, we were expected to do just the opposite — at least until everybody had been doing it for several years. And although it wasn't in print, this meant not wearing worldly adornment. This was especially hard on us girls for it meant we could not curl our hair or wear lipstick; we must appear just as God made us. We could not wear jewelry of any kind — no soul-winner would wear earrings! How could God use a person as "worldly" as that?

When other high school girls were wearing sleeveless dresses, we wore long sleeves to the wrist. When ankle socks were in, we wore long black stockings. When bobbed hair was in style,

we continued to wear long hair — done up
with hairpins!

Colors? Certainly, even color came under the
dictatorship of what it meant to be "right with
God" and to be "spiritual" (a quality greatly
to be desired). No bright colors — only quiet,
dark, drab shades.

Failure to conform held an unspoken threat:
the end result would be falling from grace and
getting away from God. Our church, with its
rules, would protect the youth from this present
evil world and all ungodliness.

But how could my will ever be God's will?
The laws and rules for Christian behavior allowed
no choice. How, then, could God guide me in
all things? Someone else was always making
up my mind for me. There seemed to be no
area in which I could make a decision of my own.
There just were no alternatives.

During those early years of my Christian life,
my security lay in conformity based on obedience.
No wonder I developed an aversion to that word.
In the following matters I could make a choice and
thus obey: church attendance, daily devotions,
conformity in dress, and abstinence from worldly
pleasures. On the other hand, by failing to do
any of these, I was disobedient, fallen from
grace, counted as a backslider needing to be
saved all over again.

Chapter 3

*Because of my need for security
and my desire to excel, I invented
more rigorous rules than I had been
taught. If a few rules were good,
more would be better. This life
style made me a pious pharisee and
a ruthless judge of other people.*

*My life was changed radically,
however, when I discovered that
God really loved me. He had only
two rules:* Love me and love your
brother as yourself. *Released from
regulations that condemn and stifle
me, I am free to love: to love
God, to love myself, and to love you!*

Ben Johnson
The Road to Freedom

FALLING FROM GRACE

The back rows of our little church were usually reserved, by mutual consent, for teen-agers who had "fallen from grace" — that is, backsliders. The aim of the Sunday evening evangelistic meeting was to sing, pray, and preach until the Spirit moved upon the backsliders, motivating them to come forward to the altar of prayer and get saved again. I know all the verses of "I Surrender All" and "Almost Persuaded"; we sang them over so many times.

It was no credit to me that I was not a perpetual backslider. The fear of God, my parents, and the preacher's wife, plus the ability to keep my mouth shut, must have kept me away from those back seats.

Many of my friends were there periodically. They failed to do the things they were supposed to do and did the things they should not have

done. That is, they failed to keep God's laws and
the rules of the church. Failure on those two
issues was sin, and when you sinned you were
a backslider.

The explanation went like this: If you lie,
you are a liar. If you steal, you are a thief.
If you sin, you are a sinner. For sin is "willful
disobedience to the known will of God."
When you sin, you immediately fall from grace
(favor with God) and need to get back into
grace again.

Human nature being as it is, those of us
who were caught in such a hapless system know
the ease with which one fell from grace. If you
have never been exposed to such religious
acrobatics, you probably marvel that we took it
week after week. wondering who would be next.
You must remember that we were minors, and
most of our parents were members of the church.
Besides, being right with God held great
promise for youthful idealists.

We were taught that small faults, mistakes,
etc. were due to human frailty and didn't count.
Those were unintentional, resulting from
inadequate knowledge or from not paying
sufficient attention. We were not required to
admit or confess them unless, of course, we had
intentionally hurt someone.

Intention was very important. It was only
good manners to apologize for a hurt of any kind.
We thought God overlooked those unintentional
ones because He knew we didn't mean them.
However, I later learned that sin is not forgiven
because of our good intentions, but because of
what Christ did on the cross.

The problem was that what was small to
one person might seem large to another and vice

versa. Does God classify sins? Or are they all
the same in His sight? Didn't Christ die for
all our sins?

> . . . *the proof of God's amazing love is this: that it*
> *was while we were sinners that Christ died for us.*
>
> — Romans 5:8, J. B. Phillips

However, when the "little" ones were
never properly taken care of (by confession), the
net result slowly grew into a backlog of
unacknowledged guilt that became unbearable.

I seldom felt that I needed to go forward
during the altar call, but I watched my friends
make frequent trips to the altar where they were
reclaimed and reinstated in grace.

And then a painful experience in my late
teens began to bring more questions from me but
fewer answers from the church. No amount of
rationalization helped in this situation. I knew
in my heart I was guilty. Should I go forward
when the altar call was given? What for? I had
already called on the Lord, and He had heard
me, helped me, and forgiven me. So why did I
have to go up there — in front of everybody?

The unending dialogue went on within me.
But if they knew, you'd go forward for prayer.
Well, what could *they* do for me? *It's your pride.*
Yes, of course. But that settled nothing.

Guilt resulting from secrecy and group
pressure is hard to contain. If I had kept my
mouth shut, I'd have saved myself a lot of grief.
But I finally told my Sunday school teacher
(the minister's wife). Then I *was* in the doghouse
(mostly, it seemed to me, of her displeasure)
and did go forward for prayer. What for? To
please and satisfy her. To be forgiven?

No, for God had already forgiven me.

Was it really necessary to tell? Was it really necessary to get saved all over again? I couldn't figure out the connection. But I determined that if there was a next time, I would hold my peace. God Himself was enough for me. I'd have dealings directly with Him, not with people.

Even at that time, although I could not state or explain it, I knew subconsciously that I was still God's child, even though His disobedient child. He did not kick me out the back door and disinherit me before I was somehow fit to come in the front door once again. God was not very "big" to me in those days, except to judge and condemn me. My own failures seemed much bigger.

In the meantime, I was trying to interpret the confusion of *being human* by stretching my inadequate knowledge of God over personal experiences, while God was trying to show me, through my heart, what He is really like.

God's love held me through all those years.

Chapter 4

People's characters are tested
in three ways: by the circumstances
in which they live, by the people
whom they meet, and by the experience
of their own failures. Their
characters are tested by the degree
in which these things draw forth
from them love and not bitterness,
a humble penitence, and dependence
upon God and not despair.

Father Andrew
A Gift of Light

BEING SANCTIFIED

The teaching of the precarious position of
continually being able to fall from grace was
not without hope. It was counterbalanced by a
second benefit or "second blessing" which ensured
the believer a fruitful and holy walk with God.
This blessing was synonymous with being filled
with the Holy Spirit.

In our little church one meeting a week was
reserved for the preaching on "scriptural holiness,"
which meant setting forth texts on the doctrine
of entire sanctification. At that time the altar was
open for those who wished to seek and to receive.

Sanctification means to set apart, to cleanse,
or to make holy. This was taught not as a
growing experience, but as a crisis experience
in which the believer was immediately cleansed
from sin and filled with the Holy Spirit.

This is not to be confused with the "baptism

of the Spirit" which is taught in the charismatic movement and also by the Pentecostal churches as an experience every believer must have after conversion. To the outside world these groups are usually classified together, but this was not true of our church, for to us "speaking in tongues" was false doctrine.

I was promised that the following list of benefits would accompany this crisis experience, and being in my late teens, I already had enough conflicts and doubts to make me ready to accept anything preached from the Bible which would meet my need.

1. Sanctification was God's will for me.
2. My conscience would be purged from the root of sin and the *want-to* would be removed, thus ensuring a maximum of security.
3. I would be prepared for the Second Coming of Christ.
4. The fruits of the Holy Spirit would then be present in my life, especially love.
5. I would be given power to be a witness for Jesus.
6. I would have holiness of heart, which the Bible says is necessary to get to heaven.
7. Sanctification and salvation were both included in the Atonement; therefore, both are available and necessary.

   (For Scripture references on which these seven benefits were based, see the *Study Manual,* Chapter 4.)

All these promises of such an abundant life were refreshing to my troubled heart,

and I was ready immediately to seek the experience. After all my struggles with absolute standards of right and wrong, plus laws and regulations meant to keep me in the straight and narrow, the sermons on being sanctified seemed the ultimate in achieving a close and steady walk with God. My heart longed for that more than I can tell you.

To do the will of God daily from a pure heart, to know the plan of God for my life work, to have a heart filled with love for God and man were goals worth any conditions.

Always quick to respond to a spiritual challenge, especially when it holds promise of drawing me nearer to Jesus, I found myself at the altar of prayer — a candidate for entire sanctification. For the promise is:

> *Blessed are they which do hunger and thirst after righteousness: for they shall be filled.*
>
> — Matthew 5:6, KJV

Someone came to pray with me to see if I had fulfilled the conditions.

"Is there any unfinished business between you and the Lord?" (I couldn't think of any.) "Any unconfessed sins? Anything to make right?" (I couldn't think of any, as I had carefully gone over all those items.) Then my counselor turned to Romans 12:1, 2 and read the verses aloud to help me make my full consecration:

> *I appeal to you therefore . . . by the mercies of God, to present your bodies as a living sacrifice, holy and acceptable to God, which is your spiritual worship.*
>
> *Do not be conformed to this world but be transformed by the renewal of your mind, that*

*you may prove what is the will of God, what is
good and acceptable and perfect.*

— Romans 12:1, 2, RSV

The will of God was being sanctified, the
scriptural proof for this being 1 Thessalonians 4:3.

I was asked: "Are you willing to give yourself
completely to God? Past, present, future? Body,
soul, and spirit? Everything you have or ever
hope to have? Will you pray and tell God this in
your own words?" I would and I did (a spiritual
exercise beneficial to all who follow it).

I was instructed to claim the promise by faith
and believe the cleansing work was done within
me. Then the Spirit would be poured upon me.
When nothing happened, I was told to come
back the next night and continue to seek until
the "witness" or assurance came. This was
usually in the form of some feeling of blessing
or joy.

I distinctly remember one illustration the
preacher used. He said our hearts could be
compared to a barrel needing to be purified from
some foreign substance. Fire — a symbol of the
Holy Spirit — would be applied by God, and all
the dross and guilt of sin would be consumed.
For while the barrel would not burn, it would
be cleansed as by fire for the Master's use.

As I knelt at the altar that night, I could
visualize my heart as a barrel with the torch being
applied and the flames consuming and burning
out all the evil within me (i.e., the old nature of
sin). Then I would be clean, and the Holy
Spirit would fill and overflow me, making me
fit for the Master's use.

I subsequently sought, found, and lost this
experience at least four distinct times during

the next ten years. I never did receive the
overwhelming "blessing" which some people did,
but nevertheless I enjoyed a quiet heart and
continued to lay foundations of daily Bible
reading, prayer, and faithful church attendance.
I was conforming, and in so doing found a
certain acceptance and belonging.

However, the ups and downs greatly disturbed
me. So, taking a piece of paper, I tried to
analyze why I had lost the experience and
studied how I could keep it.

Yes, it was there in the Bible (1 Thessalonians
4:3) ; it was God's will for me to be sanctified,
so what was wrong with me that I couldn't keep
it? I prayed for God's light to show me so
that I could obey perfectly.

True, other people seemed to lose the
experience, too, but some didn't. We could
usually tell who the "victorious" ones were by
whether they were on the outside of the altar
rail for counseling or on the inside doing
the counseling.

Perhaps the problem lay in my motivation:
so I began to check there.

The first time, my motive was to be cleansed
from the nature of sin. When I found the
sin-taint was still active, I was back at the altar
again — not only to be sanctified, but to get
saved first. I had to start all over, for I had been
taught that any sins committed must be dealt
with first and the relationship restored before
I was again a candidate for sanctification.

Now that I am writing this, I wonder why
I didn't question the whole unsatisfactory
arrangement. But where would I have gone?
To whom would I have talked? As far as I knew,
there was nobody in our little town who had

any more of God's truth than our church.

The second time, my motive went deeper. I told myself that I shouldn't seek to be rid of sin just so life would be easier and without troubles. I should seek to be made entirely holy because this would please God, not seeing that pride was behind this also. I rechecked my restitutions and consecrations to see if I had missed anything. Every little thing came under scrutiny — even stealing a spoonful of face powder from my aunt when she visited us at Christmas time.

The third time, my motive was to receive power so that I could be a witness (and thus useful) to Christ. I was not a soul-winner, and I wanted to be one. So I sought again and by faith received again.

The fourth time, I remember telling the Lord that if only He would sanctify me wholly, through and through, burn out all the dross and make me holy, I would dedicate myself to doing His will, not mine, for the rest of my life.

Chapter 5

*Now glory be to God who by his
mighty power at work within us
is able to do far more than we
would ever dare to ask or even
dream of — infinitely beyond our
highest prayers, desires, thoughts,
or hopes.*

Ephesians 3:20
The Living Bible

BEING CALLED

Immediately after I finished high school, and after much prayer, it was decided that I should attend a Bible school so that my faith might be firmly grounded before I went on to college — a place where "rank liberalism and atheism flourished."

The school chosen was one which my pastor and his wife had attended, and although it turned out to be as full of legalism and conformity as the little church to which I belonged, there were some redeeming factors.

One was that it was there that the "call from God," for which I'd been praying and waiting, came to me. Interestingly enough, it was a book that influenced my thinking, and through this experience and others I have come to believe that His voice is more often heard in the quietness of reading than in the noisiness of speaking.

A shortened edition of the life of J. Hudson Taylor, founder of the great China Inland Mission (now known as the Overseas Missionary Fellowship), was assigned as outside reading for one of my classes. While I was reading the book, one portion of it spoke to me personally.

As I remember it, Mr. Taylor was preaching one night in a small mission with an earthen floor and an open front. During his message he noticed a young man come in and sit down toward the back. By his clothing it was evident that he was a student from an upper-class home. Afterwards he waited while the other listeners filed out, and then he spoke to Mr. Taylor.

"Sir, your talk contains truth which I've never heard before. Could we speak more about it?"

They did, and in the course of their conversation the young man finally said, "How long have you known this truth of God's love, of sending Jesus, His Son, to bear our sins?"

"All my life," Mr. Taylor answered.

"And your father before you, did he know?"

"Yes."

"And your grandfather?"

"Yes, he knew also."

"And his father before him?"

"Yes," said Mr. Taylor, "they all knew."

"Then why did it take you so long to come over here and tell us? Our family owns a large shipping company. My father, and my grandfather before him, visited many countries here in the East, from India and on through Malaysia, searching for truth and never finding it. Always we knew there must be more. Why did it take you so long?"

Through that recorded incident, God spoke

to me; and already open to the guidance of
the Spirit, I responded. The Chinese people
ceased to be a mysterious race (sometimes called
heathen) ; they became flesh and blood people
who sought for truth and the meaning of life,
just as I did.

I had never considered myself a person
having any abilities or gifts, since I didn't sing or
play an instrument. But I could talk, couldn't I?
I could tell the story of Jesus and His love,
couldn't I?

Suddenly I realized what was happening.
This was it! This was my call from God. My
prayers had been answered (and my mother's).
He did need me. I could be useful and serve Him.
There, alone in my room on my knees,
I settled it all.

Yes, I was willing to go to China as a
missionary. Everything else could go. I counted
the cost mentally, willing to give up at that
moment everything of value to me: my home,
my loved ones, college next year — yes,
everything I could think of.

Later, when I went to lunch and began to
tell my friends about my experience and decision,
I felt even more joy and assurance that China
was where God wanted me. I wrote to my parents
about it, and they rejoiced with me.

In two years' time I had finished the Bible
course, taken a short secretarial course, and at
twenty years of age was on my way to South
China to be a secretary for a mission in Canton.
But before I sailed, I had that experience with
the college girls with which I began this book —
the experience which caused me so much
disturbance with regard to my message and
its incompleteness.

Chapter 6

There is always more waiting up ahead...
for God is in all our tomorrows,
as well as our yesterdays,
and His love and purpose toward us
never change.

R.R.

MY DISCOVERY BEGINS

At the end of my first seven-year term in China I did some solid thinking during my voyage back to the U.S.A. I was dissatisfied with the kind of Christian life I was living and the results of the secretarial work I had been doing in China. What did those seven years really amount to? My passport said "missionary," but I wasn't much of a missionary. What had I done for God? I certainly hadn't made any converts to Christ because my work had all been in the missionary office.

Defending myself, I replied, *Well, how could I have any more contact with the Chinese than I did?* Yes, I knew the students and teachers and pastors, but only casually.

My conscience continued to prod me: What about those young salesmen in the Chinese art stores? They were always ready to practice their English when three or four of us arrived almost every Saturday. True, I might have — I could have — approached them or at least given them something to read. But I didn't.

Taking inventory of growth in my spiritual life, I didn't come up with much more satisfaction either. At least I was wiser. I had learned to watch my fellow-workers who weren't any more perfect than I was and who did not keep "throwing over" their sanctified experience. I learned the art of rationalization in order to protect myself and my precious experience. I learned to examine my motives because God knew (didn't He?) all things, and He knew my heart was set on doing His will. I became the world's best rationalizer and, sorry to say, that dubious achievement still clings to me.

However, if good motives are enough, then why did Christ have to come and die for sin? I didn't see this truth then. I learned it the hard way. It seems that despite my cheerful disposition, the only way God can ever teach me anything and get my full attention is by letting me hit bottom good and hard.

I was to learn that the centrality of Jesus Christ is more important than any truth in the Christian faith. I also was to learn that the answer to my personal needs is in Him, not in my own feelings, motives, and experiences.

How did I learn this? By getting myself caught in an emotional triangle and emerging the rejected one. My motives were fine, but my emotions and actions were not.

It was a bitter struggle. Even my basic faith in God's goodness and the veracity of the Bible came into question. I remember hearing a duet in church, *"Christ is not* a disappointment. Every

longing in my heart finds in Him complete
fulfillment. He is all the world to me," or words
to that effect. I sat there denying all I heard.
Christ *was* a disappointment. I should have said
that being "holy" was a disappointment, but
at that time I was still putting Christ and the
experience together as one. I had not yet
discovered the Person of Jesus Christ or the
full message of the Work of Christ.

My thoughts went on: *Every longing in my
heart did not find fulfillment. Not in Christ it
didn't. He certainly is not all in all to me.
The words of that song are not true. They are
just words. Mere words.*

Suddenly appalled at the thoughts I was
thinking, I quietly left the church and went
back to my apartment. It was true. All these years
I had served God and tried to do what He
wanted me to do, and now when I wanted
something very much — I was left holding the
bag. *Well,* my inner self said, *are you trying
to bargain with God?*

As the days went by I was aware that the
bottom had really dropped out of my life.
Was there any faith left? Yes, God was there.
Once again, in the midst of a crowd of people,
I remember finding refuge in a small clothes closet
where I cried out my failure and frustration to
God. If He didn't help me, if He couldn't help
me, why live any longer? The meaning had
simply dropped out of my life.

Some quietness came after that as I realized
I was putting God to the test. Either He was
enough and His love was sufficient, or He wasn't.
My mind said: of course He is enough; all through
the ages He's been enough. But my heart said:
He has to be enough for me — for me, Ros Rinker.

This went on for about three months.
Three drab, cold, colorless, dragging months.
Every night I said, "Lord, are You enough?"
And every morning I repeated it, "Lord,
are You enough?"

Just at this time a book fell into my hands
which gave me a strong ray of hope. It was a red
paperback, *Hudson Taylor's Spiritual Secret* —
the story of the growth and establishing of
Taylor's walk with God through suffering in his
spirit and through his circumstances.

On this particular occasion, due to an
epidemic which claimed several of their children,
Mrs. Taylor left for England with the remaining
children. There Taylor was, alone in China
with those graves on the hillside. It finally became
more than he could bear, and day after day in
his desperation he cried out to God. The
answer must be there. It had to be there. It was!

The answer came to him through reading
the Scriptures, particularly John 4:13, 14 and
John 7:37-39.

> *Everyone who drinks this water will be thirsty
> again. But whoever drinks the water I will give
> him will never be thirsty again. For my gift will
> become a spring in the man himself, welling
> up into eternal life.*

> — John 4:13, 14, J. B. Phillips

I still remember those words: "Never means
never, and will means will, and thirsty means
any unsatisfied need." If Hudson Taylor
could take hold of that promise and find it to be
true, so could I. I memorized those verses.
I studied the whole chapter, taking particular
notice of the two kinds of water: that from the

earthly well and that from the spiritual well.
I believed it. I clung to it. I waited for it.

Then one Sunday morning I awoke with
the sun streaming into my windows. It was a
beautiful day, and I wanted to get dressed and
into that sunshine. Pulling on my clothes, I found
a song on my lips and I was amazed! I recognized
that what I was singing was true. Every word of it!

> *Jesus is dearer than all to me,*
> *His only His I'll be.*

It was a gift from God! I didn't do a thing
to earn it, or attain it, or even deserve it! It
wasn't given because of my prayers or faithfulness
in reading my Bible because I hadn't been
faithful in either during those months. I was an
orphan — alone, unloved, rejected. His love,
like the ocean waves, broke over me again and
again. I was His. He did love me. I belonged
to Him. He was enough. Deep within me I knew
it was Jesus Christ, my Savior and my God, who
loved me. He knew all about rejection and
aloneness. He, Himself, was the important one,
not any experience I got or lost through
obedience or disobedience.

How can words tell any more than I've
just told!

My whole life took on a new tone. I began
to read my Bible because I wanted to know just
what Jesus was actually like, what He said,
what He did — all about Him. Always before
I had read my Bible to be faithful at devotions,
to find verses to memorize, or to lead a class.

Someone asked me, "Were you a Christian
then?" Of course I was. I accepted Christ when
I was fifteen years old and was born into His
family. This was a new revelation of Him. I didn't

know it then, but there were more revelations coming up in later years. Which is as it should be.

I was learning that the answer to life is not in my own holiness, but in Christ Himself. It was another fifteen years before I actually grasped the fact that any degree of stability must include: (1) the nature and character of God, and (2) the scope of the Atonement of Christ.

There is always more waiting up ahead . . . for God is in all our tomorrows, as well as our yesterdays, and His love and purpose toward us never change.

Chapter 7

*We can only know true freedom
when we are secure enough
to admit our failure
and call it sin, knowing
that the relationship
never changes
and
that immediate confession
restores the fellowship.*

R.R.

Confession: Renewal

Since that painful experience as a teen-ager,
I had avoided the subject of confession like the
proverbial plague. But in China during my
second term, God finally brought me face to
face with it, and it began to activate a new era
in my Christian life and ministry.

One of my first memories relating to confession
concerns the revival which came to students
of our Bible institute in Shanghai. We had heard
them praying throughout the night, and the next
morning chapel was never dismissed. They
continued through the afternoon and into the
evening; they continued on through that night
and all the next day. They didn't even stop to
eat their meals.

Those of us who worked in the mission
office soon learned what was going on and what
had triggered it. The night before our large bus

had taken the students into the city to hear
Dr. John Sung preach.

Dr. Sung was God's man (the Billy Graham
of China) for those pre-Communist years.
Multitudes of people came into the kingdom
of God through his preaching. Educated in
America, earning his Ph.D. with honors, John
Sung was converted while in America when he
read the New Testament through for the first
time. He vowed that when he returned to his
homeland, he would preach the Gospel.

Dr. Sung always used graphic illustrations.
On this particular night he had said: "You people
look fine — hair combed, clothes clean — very
respectable. But how does God see you? He looks
at your heart. What does He see? I'll show you."

At that point he unbuttoned his blue outer
garment and stood exposed in an inner white
one covered with writing — big black Chinese
characters which named all kinds of sins. He
tried hiding behind the pulpit, but the choir
could see him. He tried hiding on either side
of the pulpit, but the crowd sitting on the
platform steps could see him. There was no
place to hide.

"Until you make confession and restitution
for sins and put your trust wholly in Jesus
Christ, you are guilty! You are lost and you
need a Savior. . . ."

This meeting had precipitated the revival
among our students. That first evening some of
us missionaries went into the chapel to listen.
There seemed to be a pattern to what was
going on, but there was no human leader.
It was a Spirit-led meeting.

One person would say, "Pray for me,"
and a wave of audible prayer was heard. Then

in great agony of spirit, often with tears of contrition and shame, the person who had requested prayer would tell his story and confess his sins — sometimes from a kneeling position, sometimes standing. I remember one man who wrote his sins on the blackboard.

Not knowing the language at that time, we waited for Clara to interpret for us, which, although it was done in a whisper, attracted the attention of the students. One young man finally stood and addressed us with a pointed finger.

"You foreigners back there — wanting to know what *our* sins are — why don't you confess your sins? Then you would have God's peace and blessing as we do. But no, you are too self-sufficient, too foreign, too proud! At least you could be quiet and pray for us."

Feeling much condemned, one by one we quietly left the chapel. But why should we confess our sins before those Chinese students? We had already confessed our sins to God and He had forgiven us — or so we said.

The Oxford Group

A few years after that experience, I had another confrontation with confession which I succeeded in avoiding. I was vacationing in Pei-tai-ho, the North China seaside resort where many missionaries gathered during the summer months. Soon it became rumored that a team of men and women from the Oxford Group was there for the summer holding closed meetings, but anyone wishing to attend could easily get an invitation.

They were a group of people originally

from Oxford University in England who gave
personal testimony to what God was doing in
their lives and by this means urged others to hear
God speak. They "listened to God" in a quiet
hour each morning and were always telling what
happened as a result.

They emphasized four principles which they
used as standards for life: absolute honesty,
absolute purity, absolute unselfishness, and
absolute love. And then came the esoteric catch:
to gain freedom and live by the absolutes and
hear God speak, one must confess the exact
nature of his lifetime wrongs to at least one
person — one who had already gone through
this ordeal.

We all balked at this. I don't remember the
exact reactions of others, but I remember mine.
God had already forgiven all my sins; why drag
them out now? It smacked of the confessional.
At any rate, our mission did not agree with
their teaching, and I was thereby protected.
I refused to be exposed. Secretly I said to myself:
Wild horses couldn't drag it out of me. I really
believed God had forgiven me, that all my
sins were in the sea of His forgetfulness, so why
bring them up again? It would not only
distress me, but how could it glorify God?

Later when I heard that missionaries from
the Presbyterian, Lutheran, Methodist, and
Episcopal churches were being converted through
the activities of the Oxford Group, I took
further satisfaction in my fabricated refuge.
People in our mission were already "converted
and sanctified" and didn't need to go through
psychological excesses.

With that, I dismissed the subject a
second time.

Robert F. Rinker, age 29

Lydia M. Rinker, age 25

Denise Rinker (left), age 1 year,
and Rosalind (right), age 2½

Rinker family, 1914: from left, Rosalind,
Ralph, Franklin, Lydia, Denise

Rosalind's passport picture
for China, 1926

Rosalind during
China years, 1940

Photograph used for Rosalind's first Zondervan book,
Prayer—Conversing With God, 1958

Chapter 8

I was free to serve my Lord. . . .
A great freedom!
I didn't have to label it with any theological
term or define it as any special "experience."
I simply enjoyed the celebration, the joyous
weightlessness of a free spirit.

R.R.

CONFESSION: OBEDIENCE

Then God broke through my resistance and changed the whole course of my life through a Presbyterian nurse, Orpha Gould.

I first met Orpha when as a missionary secretary in Peking I was invited to attend a tea which was held at the home of one of our missionaries. Coming in late, I found the only seat left was beside an American woman wearing Chinese clothes, her hair wound in a braid around her head. She was the only one there not wearing American clothes. In the course of our conversation, I asked if she would mind a personal question. She didn't.

"Why are you dressed that way?"

"Oh, these clothes?" She explained, "I've given most of my American ones away. And since I work with a team of Chinese girls in the villages, I wear these all the time."

Now I was intensely interested because

I didn't know any missionaries who served the
Lord in the villages — or who wore Chinese
clothes all the time! The ones I knew lived in
big cities and worked in schools, hospitals, or in
offices, like myself. I questioned her the whole
time. Did she eat Chinese food? Did people
come to know Jesus? Were their lives changed?
Yes, yes, yes, to all those questions. And then there
were more questions.

Almost a year later I wrote a letter to Orpha,
asking if I could go with her and her team
into the mountain villages that summer — for
that's where they went, instead of to Pei-tai-ho
or some other resort.

The events which led to the writing of that
letter were used by God to bring me to a new
quality of life and a renewed call to service.

Learning to Hear

First, there was an unexpected operation
for adhesions from a former operation; then a
sudden embolism left me hovering between life
and death for one solid week. I remember
awaking one night and finding Dr. Harry W.
Miller sitting by my bed.

"What are you doing here?" I asked.

"Wondering why you are still here," was
his frank reply. He even slept on a cot on the
porch outside my door during that time.
At the end of the week when he left the porch,
he said to me, "Young lady, I didn't pull you
through this. God has given you a second chance."

The recuperation time lengthened into
three months. As I grew stronger, one morning
I was asked to speak to the Chinese students in
chapel. Looking through *My Utmost for His*

Highest by Oswald Chambers for favorite
passages already marked, I chose one on "hearing
the voice of God." As I closed my remarks and
wanted some action to show intention, I asked
all who would take time to listen to God that
day to raise their hands. Suddenly I realized
I was the only one there who had not raised
a hand, and my hand went up too.

Walking back to my room, I knew I was
on the spot. I had promised to let God speak to
me. What did He want to say? Was I ready
to listen?

I had lunch, took a nap, tried to read a
magazine, threw it on the floor, thought about
going shopping, and finally slipped to my
knees beside the bed.

"All right, Lord Jesus, You win. I'll listen.
Whatever You say." In that split second I thought
of Orpha Gould and knew that I should go
with her to the villages and teach the people
about Jesus. Wasn't that what my first calling
was all about? Telling others — those who
had never heard — about Jesus?

Once more I attempted to push it aside.
I went out and found my good friend Esther
Erny and said, "I think I'm well. I want to take
the train back to Shanghai (I was in Peking).
I need to get back to work. Do you think I
could leave tomorrow night?"

We were walking through one of the beautiful
covered roof-ways which surrounded a lovely
rock-pool in the garden. Esther took one look
at me. "What's wrong with you, Rosalind?"

I told her about my struggle, and she did
the kindest thing any person can do for another.
She said, "Come on in and we'll pray together
about it."

We got on our knees, and she prayed for me.
Then — there on my knees — I remembered
the difficult privations of village life: no hot
water, no running water, cornstalk-lined holes
for toilets — and I was ashamed. For then I
remembered the Lord Jesus: He came on a
mission, was rejected and killed, but rose again.
His words came back to me: *"I will be with you
all the way. I send you, and I will take care
of you."* Once again God was demonstrating to
me His communicating love.

This was my second call, right in line with
the first one, but so real and so definite that
I began to make plans to implement it.
I wrote that letter to Orpha about joining her
for her summer trip.

Learning Obedience

Back at the Shanghai office I was open to
God's directions. I made it a special daily project
to hear what He had to say to me.

*"My sheep hear my voice, and I know them,
and they follow me"* (John 10:27).

I couldn't begin to tell you all that He told
me. I even wrote everything down — all the
things I heard! All the things I did because
I believed He wanted me to — no arguing this
time. Often I've marveled at the kindness of our
Lord. Knowing my objections to verbal
confession, He wisely led me into other paths
of obedience first.

For instance, there was my pride, which was
leveled when I had to make restitution and
acknowledgments of wrong attitudes and acts.
My money — giving up the right to say where
it should be spent. I had been a strict tither,

but never had I given any gifts beyond the tithe.
That was soon changed, too. My possessions —
too many clothes and shoes which I didn't wear.
I began to give them away. My few household
items (the mission furnished the big items of
furniture) — rugs, dishes, pictures. One night
when my two roommates were out, God
spoke to me through my thoughts.

"You are going into China's villages to preach
the Gospel. They have nothing, compared to
you. Hard dirt floors, paper windows, brick beds.
How can you own all these treasures and
pretend to live like one of them? If you go with
Orpha, what will you do with these things?"

"Well, Lord, what shall I do?" I asked.

His answer came right back. "Go, sell all
that you have, and come and follow Me."

Did He really mean that? I looked at those
Peking rugs I loved; the carved stools which
felt like satin to the touch; those lovely pictures —
the one was irreplaceable. Suddenly I was on
my knees again, ashamed and repentant.
Then I looked at my possessions again. They
were still lovely, but they weren't mine anymore.
The next morning I told the girls, and they
were eager to buy everything.

But where was an answering letter from
Orpha? Here I was getting ready to go to the
villages, and no word yet from her. What if . . . ?
A dozen questions tortured me. I firmly
disregarded them and gave thanks to God.
He was my Good Shepherd, and I was following
Him. He would make the way plain in His
own time. Finally the letter came — the day
came — when I got on the train for Pao-ting-fu
and my first trip to China's villages.

In Pao-ting-fu, Orpha and the Chinese girls

in her team took me shopping. We began to make
Chinese clothes and bedding which could be
used in the villages. I learned to eat Chinese
food twice a day. Fellowship, sharing, and
praying became our daily procedure.

Then that old subject of confession came up
again. One morning, fresh from her time alone
with God, Orpha came to me with a question.

"Rosalind, do you know how to help these
Chinese women come to Jesus? Shall I teach you
how? The way that seems to help them most is
to take the Ten Commandments and go right
down the list, asking: 'Did you do this?'
and explaining what it means. They don't know
what is sin and what isn't. We teach them to
confess, to repent, and to accept forgiveness
right there. That establishes a way of life and
growth for them after we've gone."

I listened with a growing knot in my
stomach as she continued.

"Have you ever done this? If you haven't,
it is going to be hard on you when they do it, for
all you will think of will be the times you
broke the commandments and never told."

"You sound like the Oxford Group to me,"
I countered. "Confession of sins to human beings
instead of to God!" It was pure self-defense,
and her answer shattered me.

"I've never heard of the Oxford Group.
Who are they?"

Briefly I explained and then asked why she
used "open" confession as a means of bringing
the villagers to Christ. Orpha then told me
the story of her conversion. Sitting under the
ministry of Dr. John Sung and following his
instructions on confession, she had become a new
person in Christ. She had been transformed

from a nominal missionary nurse into a new child in the family of God.

Losing My Life

I went out alone to walk and pray and think. Twice before I had rejected confession — at that student revival and again at Pei-tai-ho — and here I was faced with it once more. I was learning the important lesson that God is faithful in His love, care, and planning, even when I turned Him down continually on some subject. In His patient loving-kindness He brought it back again and again. And I really didn't want to escape from His love. I wanted to do His will.

Why, then, was the human part of me so opinionated? *Because,* said my inner voice, *there is fear, stubbornness, shame, and risk.*

To mortify the flesh and gain a little time, I went out with a bucket of hot suds and a mop and cleaned the outdoor toilet. And let God talk to me — which He did, through a well-known verse of Scripture.

> *Whosoever will save his life shall lose it; but whosoever shall lose his life for my sake and the gospel's, the same shall save it.*
>
> — Mark 8:35, KJV

To relate the exact nature of my failures and wrongdoings to Orpha when I was getting ready to be her co-worker would actually be losing my life: my self-respect, my pride, my good opinion of myself, and her good opinion of me. Some people knew one thing, some another; some things nobody knew. But to put it all together in one telling! That would be losing my life for sure!

"Lord, I've gone this far, and You've helped me and seen me through. You've got me in a corner this time. I give up. I don't need any more Scripture, any more theology, any more arguments for or against. I'll do it."

And I did. It took me less than ten minutes to tell what I considered the worst — ten awful minutes of hemming and hawing and letting the last vestige of pride die (or so I thought). But I hadn't considered what would happen when the dam finally broke! The next three days were dark and humiliating as I remembered one little miserable thing after another which had completely slipped my mind.

I promised God that whatever came to my mind, whatever He let me remember, I would tell. Out with it — forever!

I came to know the meaning and the bitter taste of repentance for the first time. When I accepted Christ as a teen-ager, I only knew the basic meaning of repentance: to turn from my way to God's way. Now I saw the error of my ways as I turned anew to Him with sorrow in my heart for having grieved Him and having missed His way. For the first time in my life I knew the hopelessness of the nature of sin: that source within me from which all the acts emanated.

It was a thorough housecleaning. I was spent and empty, but quiet and clean — like a little child.

We went to the mountain villages of Hopei Province that summer, and I was free to serve my Lord: free to help His little ones, free to help others admit their sins, free to praise and worship and walk with Jesus. A great freedom! I didn't have to label it with any theological term or define it as any special "experience."

I simply enjoyed the celebration, the joyous weightlessness of a free spirit.

Learning Balance

When I returned to Peking, I shared with other missionaries what had happened to me. They weren't at all impressed. Then, in the will of God, two missionaries from South Africa, Aletta Jacobsz and Eunice Marais, came to us with exactly the same message on confession and restitution.

There was a fresh revival among many missionaries in China and Korea resulting from their ministry.

It was at this time that I read everything I could lay my hands on regarding confession, so sure was I that this was the open door to true freedom in Christ. Not sinless perfection, but walking in the light, in openness before God and man, ready to admit failure and not hide it away.

There I was — stepping right into the old conformity trap and insisting that what had been good for me would also be good for everybody, if only they would try it. For three years after returning from China on my second furlough, I took meetings everywhere I was invited, teaching complete confession of sin by making lists as Miss Jacobsz had taught us, using the verses she compiled, called Heart-Searching Scriptures. (See *Prayer — Conversing with God,* Appendix, pg. 113, Zondervan Publishing House, 1959.)

It was not until several years later when the revelation of the completed work of Christ on the cross was revealed to me that I toned down the confession message; for then I saw that

God accepts us totally on the basis of Jesus Christ's Atonement — He became God's Lamb for the whole world. If one is saved by confession, then it becomes "works" that we do, which can never save anyone.

So the balance came, and I began to see the place confession rightfully has in a believer's life. Not for any bargaining with God to obtain a high spiritual experience, but for a life of openness and freedom, for love and fellowship. Another name for this is "the healing of memories," a term used by Agnes Sanford in her lectures and books. Sometimes this takes place by the laying on of hands without verbal confession. The reason such an experience becomes necessary is that although we believe God forgives us, we have not forgiven ourselves or someone else.

The experience of verbal confession set me free for a personal ministry in the lives of others — in the lives of God's children who, being bound, still longed for freedom.

Chapter 9

God teaches His truth
long beforehand, and then
suddenly we are able to
look back and see the landmarks
which verify the validity of
the new truth.

R.R.

RECOGNIZING THE TRUTH

While I was helping teach rural villagers
to read during my second term, we used visual
aids to assist us. These were posters which had
been illustrated by a Chinese artist and printed
up by some united church association. They
covered a variety of New Testament subjects
and Bible verses.

Whenever it was my turn to speak, I'd search
through the big box filled with these posters.
The Scriptures or topics were written on an
outer fold, so I'd glance through them, praying
for guidance as to which one I should use.
But there was one poster I never chose:
the one with the verses from John 10:28-30.

*And I give them eternal life, and they shall
never perish, and no one shall snatch them out
of my hand. My Father, who has given them to*

> *me, is greater than all, and no one is able to*
> *snatch them out of the Father's hand. I and*
> *the Father are one.*
>
> **— RSV**

I avoided that poster because our church
did not teach this kind of security and literally
ignored those verses by teaching that I, personally,
could step out of the Father's hand at any time
and return at any time. Consequently,
I didn't know what to do with those verses.

This was not the case, however, with one
of my Chinese Presbyterian colleagues who chose
that poster frequently! So, like it or not, I had
to listen to her teach those verses in Chinese!

Let me describe the poster, for the visual
impact left as great an impression as the
verses themselves.

Black on white — standing out starkly in the
very center as the hand of God was a huge closed
fist, the arm of which faded into the background.
Held closely and securely in that fist was the
tiny figure of a man. Tied to each huge finger
and thumb were black ropes which extended
to five little devils who were attempting to pull
them open, presumably so that the man would
fall out and could then be whisked away to
whatever evil awaited him.

One look at the picture showed the
impossibility of the situation. Those little black
figures didn't have a chance. They were no
match for the great hand, pull as they might.

My friend would go into the subject,
explaining the way to come into God's family
through Christ, who is the basis of our
relationship in that family. What if one failed —
sinned? Restoration of fellowship was to be

made whenever necessary. Admit and confess
one's sins daily; keep short accounts with God.
There it was again — that sinning religion!
Did one need to sin every day of his life? I
couldn't help hearing it, but I didn't believe it —
or so I said to myself.

That poster confronted me time and again,
but I never actually acknowledged what it meant
until after the Montana visit.

The Montana Visit

When I went home on my second furlough,
I accepted an invitation to be a houseguest at
the home of Bill and Nellie Lohof in Billings,
Montana. Bill and Nellie had written me in
China and sent me gifts. Their daughter, Hilda,
had met my sister, Denise, in college, and
gradually ties between the two families
became stronger.

The Lohofs were members of a church that
taught the doctrine our church frowned upon —
that of the security of the believer. "Eternal
security" we called it. I knew this, but what could
I do about the invitation to visit them? This was
a personal friendship, and stopping over in
Montana was convenient and seemed right.
Bill and Nellie were eager to meet me and to
have me in their home as their guest.

Three things impressed me greatly during
that visit at the Lohofs. First, Bill was a
contractor, and when he came home for lunch,
he usually had a story about a witness he had
made to some workman on the job. What amazed
me was that he loved Jesus and loved people
and still believed in that "false" doctrine.

Second, when I went to church with the

Lohofs on Sunday, I was prepared to go into enemy territory and prayed for protection. Actually, I discovered that they sang the same songs we did and everyone carried Bibles. In fact, I'd never seen that many Bibles used in our church at home. Their preacher spoke from one whole chapter in the Bible, not just from certain verses he'd selected to prove his point.

The third incident took place a day or so before my departure. I got down on my knees by the bed in their guest room and turned to one of the two Scriptures I knew on the subject of security, those same verses that were on that Chinese poster (John 10:28-30). First I read them aloud and then I prayed — something like this:

"Lord, You know why I've always skipped over these verses. I don't know where this is leading, but because it is in the Bible and because the Lohofs believe it, I take it now as Your truth. I believe You can hold me in Your hand forever, and no one — not even myself — can separate me from You. Amen."

There were no flashing lights, no overwhelming blessings, but for the first time in my life I had broken through religious prejudice, the catalyst being a quality I was not to understand or recognize until years afterwards. It was simply the power of love. The Lohofs loved me.

If you think it strange that church people erect such barriers, just thank God you were never subject to them and go on your happy way. You, no doubt, have your own hang-ups, and God will deal with them — believe me He will — one by one and in great love. For God loves you just as much as He loves me.

My decision and prayer had been made
without all the usual "proofs" that most people
demand. I still had to make an honest search of
more Scripture to discover what I really believed
and what the Bible really taught. I was still
hearing the old line and comparing it to the
new truth being revealed to me.

But even the hymns of the church held
new meaning now, and I found myself wanting
to read every single line because my heart and
mind had been freed from prejudice.

> *I sought the Lord, and afterward I knew*
> *He moved my soul to seek Him, seeking me;*
> *It was not I that found, O Saviour true;*
> *No, I was found of Thee.*
>
> *Thou didst reach forth Thy hand and*
>   *mine enfold;*
> *I walked and sank not on the storm-vexed sea;*
> *'Twas not so much that I on Thee took hold,*
> *As Thou, dear Lord, on me.*
>
> *I find, I walk, I love; but O the whole*
> *Of love is but my answer, Lord, to Thee!*
> *For Thou wert long beforehand with my soul;*
> *Always Thou lovedst me.*

— George W. Chadwick

Chapter 10

We are persons to contain and manifest
the Person . . . to be free, loving, intelligent
containers of the One Person in the
universe who is the God of self-giving love
(Father, Son, and Spirit), and we find
the delight and entire satisfaction
of our created natures in being as He
is, living as He lives, loving as He loves.

Norman Grubb
God Unlimited

THE SECRET: CHRIST IN ME

The practical as well as the mystical aspects of Christ living within one of His children first came to me through a story I heard early in my second term in Shanghai while I was still working in the missionary office. We often had opportunity to hear speakers who were passing through the city. One day we learned that a certain Miss Tippett, an Englishwoman with the China Inland Mission, would be speaking at their headquarters. God had anointed her with a special gift so that great spiritual awakening and revival took place everywhere she spoke, especially out in the rural areas among the village people. That meant she was willing to endure the rigors and hardships of village life — a quality we greatly admired.

A group of us planned to go and hear Miss Tippett the following evening, but wouldn't you know — I was sick all day. So sick I couldn't even lift my head off the pillow. The others went without me.

When the two girls with whom I was living returned that evening, they came in to report on the meeting.

"Oh, it was just wonderful!"

"You should have been there, Ros. God really speaks through her."

When I wanted to know what Miss Tippett talked about, they only repeated such phrases. I insisted they tell me at least one specific thing she had said, so finally one volunteered to relate the story of a little Chinese woman.

This little woman had opened her whole life and heart for Christ to live in her to reach those around her in love and with healing. So firm was her belief that Christ lived in her that in everything she did, she first consulted Him in order that she might find the persons He wanted to love (through her).

One day she went on a shopping trip into the city of Shanghai. She needed something in notions which was on the second floor of the large Sincere Department Store. After she went through the revolving door at the entrance, she stepped over to one side for a moment.

"Lord Jesus," she prayed, "what do You want to do? Do You want to go up the elevator, or do You want to go up the stairs?"

After a moment of quiet, she started toward the door leading to a narrow stairway which would take her to the second floor. As soon as she opened the door and started up, she knew why the Lord Jesus wanted her to go up the stairs. Someone was in deep trouble. Someone seemed to be crying her life away with great, deep, racking sobs.

Hurrying to the side of the weeping woman, our little woman put an arm around her to comfort her, prayed for her, and sang aloud to her — all of which helped dispel the power of darkness and brought the presence of God near.

Soon she knew the whole story. The woman's distraught state had resulted from one of those traumatic temper fights within the family. In China, these often lasted for weeks, disrupting the whole household, making the participants ill, and sometimes even causing death. The neighbors usually came to listen to the "show" because the Chinese fight verbally more than physically. The man with the best vocabulary would win, but the bitterness within became slow poison.

The weeping woman had taken as much of the conflict as she could. Then she had left the house and found a place to pour out her own pent-up feelings. And who found her? The Lord Jesus Himself, living in our little woman.

She took the distraught woman home, put water on to boil, made soft rice porridge for the children who had not been fed, washed them and combed their hair, swept the floor, and sang songs of praise to God. The neighbors (as usual) flocked in to see what new thing was going on now and stayed to listen to the songs and to the story of God's love — the Gospel of Jesus Christ.

After the girls had told me this story and left, I closed my door and got on my knees. Thinking about that little woman, I knew I never would have asked direction; I would have gone straight to the elevator.

With a great longing and consuming desire,
I wanted Jesus to live in me as He did in that
little woman. I was tired of "trying to get an
experience," tired of trying to be "a victorious
Christian." If only Christ would live in me
like that! If only I could hear His voice like that!
If only He could reach through me to love
people who needed to be loved!

Wasn't that what being a Christian was all
about? Wasn't that what Jesus prayed for in
John 17 — that we should love one another just as
He loves us?

This simple story was like a great shining
light to give me direction. This I could do; this
I wanted to do. I could turn myself over to
Christ to be available to Him, to be a container,
to be receptive. With this living seed planted
in my heart, the other events which brought
personal conviction to me began to fit into place.

For this is God's plan:
to make known his secret to his people,
this rich and glorious secret
which he has for all peoples.
And the secret is this: Christ is in you,
which means that you will share
the glory of God.

— Colossians 1:27,
Good News for Modern Man

Chapter 11

All those searching years I thought
my problem was regarding the Holy Spirit.
Now I see
that it was the teaching on perfectionism
which hindered me from seeing the truth
within the circle of God's family:
justification and security in Christ Jesus,
who Himself is the Baptizer.

R.R.

Titus 3:5-7
Mark 1:7,8
1 Corinthians 12:13

Chapter III

SECURITY WITHIN THE CIRCLE

Unable to return to China for a third term because of political changes, I was thrust into a period of decision which taught me a great deal about finding the will of God. I learned that He guides us not only through Scripture, people, and circumstances, but through our own desires, which He plants in our hearts. All of these factors influenced my entering a small church-affiliated college. Scattered credits from other years were gathered up, and soon I was registered as a third-quarter sophomore, eventually to graduate in the class of 1945.

I enrolled in that particular college because it taught the doctrine with which I was familiar. I was still a product of that teaching and felt comfortable there. I knew the doctrine, had received the experience, and had taught it. We are what our background has made us, so in spite of knowing that I was quietly moving in another direction, I waited. I knew in my heart that I was following the guidance as far as had been given to me, and that ahead of me lay more experiences which would bring the truth into clearer focus.

Every year the college invited a special evangelist for a series of revival meetings. The messages were the familiar homilies, proving from the Bible that holiness of heart and life was scripturally sound and that any sin required repentance.

I don't remember who the speakers were during my years there, but I vividly recall the reactions of the upperclassmen around me. During the altar call when disturbed and guilty students went forward to pray, we were supposed to be praying for them — and we did. But the remarks I heard again and again disturbed me.

"There he goes. I thought he would. He'll find out just like I did — it doesn't work."

"Look at the freshmen going to that altar!" A short laugh of disillusionment. "I did the same thing as a freshman, but no more. Nothing lasts. You're just the same. Maybe worse."

Another would add, "Yup, it's the same old thing. You don't get changed at all."

And still another. "You won't catch me up there again. I've been there often enough. I'll do my praying in my own room."

My private opinion: these kids weren't getting any real help with what was bothering them. How could I help? I knew a way; should I use it? During those "transparency sessions" in China I had learned the power of honesty in confession versus the old rat race of rationalization and generalization. And during that time I also had learned how to face a specific situation and deal with it.

I knew — from personal experience — what was happening down at that altar. It was general, anonymous praying. If you cried enough tears and got shook-up enough, somehow the blessing of God through Christ was supposed to come to you. Hardly anyone ever faced up to anything definite, or at least nobody else knew what it was that shook you up. No objective therapy took place. Consequently, kids were at that altar over and over with the very same problems, and seldom was anything settled. The result was a continual load of guilt which was spiritually crippling. This continues to happen unless the Holy Spirit brings true revival, such as the one among our Chinese students.

So what did I do? I went down to that altar and knelt and prayed with the first one I came to: "What's wrong here?" I asked. "What's the trouble?" But she only cried some more. Finally, I knew what had to be done. I took that student, sat quietly apart from the others, and gave her a chance to unload and face up to her specific problem. Then I was able to help her with definite Scriptures such as 1 John 1:9.

> *If we confess our sins, he is faithful and just, and will forgive our sins and cleanse us from all unrighteousness.*
>
> — RSV

Word got around that Ros helped people with specific problems. They began to come to my dormitory room, and I loved them and prayed with them. Their needs were like mine because being members of the human race, we do not

live without sin and failure. But God does
not cast us out; He forgives us, and His
forgiveness is real.

Besides encouraging them to name and face
things, I added what I was beginning to believe
more fully myself: the truth of John 10:28-30 —
the holding power of Christ's love; and Romans
8:31-39 — the unchangeable love of God, the
family status, His constant presence with us and
within — that nothing ever separates us from Him.

These truths came like cool water to the
students; they drank them in, and I watched their
lives become stabilized in Christ's holding power.

The Kentucky Visit

While I was still a college student, I was
invited to spend a weekend visiting a small
mission and Bible school in the Kentucky
mountains. The director-founder knew my parents
in North Dakota, and he also knew our doctrine
because his sister attended our church.

I found myself relaxed and wide-open for
more knowledge. I was not on guard as I had
been during the first part of that Montana
visit with the Lohofs. This friend gave the truth
to me in such a simple form that I accepted it at
once. I guess God knew I needed it just like that.

He asked me a single loaded question: "For
how many of your sins did Christ die?"

"For all of them," I answered.

He held up three fingers and began to count.

"Past?"

"Yes."

"Present?"

"Yes."

"Future?"

"Yes, yes, of course."

I knew the answer then, before he asked the question.

"Does Jesus ever have to come and die again for the sins of the world? Will God ever change His mind about what Jesus accomplished for us on the cross?"

"Obviously not. Of course not."

The truth lay there before me, shining and bright, new and true. More Scripture began to come alive for me relating to the eternal scope of what took place at Calvary.

Romans 4:23-25: the resurrection of Jesus was God's pledge to justify us in His sight, and that was two thousand years before I was born.

Romans 5:6-11: the cross covered my sins — all of them — before I was ever born.

Hebrews 9:23-28: you'll have to read these verses for yourself to get the full impact. Briefly: Old Testament offerings were made continually, but now Christ has come, once for all men and for all time, to remove sin through the sacrifice of Himself. He need never do this again. Next time He comes it will be a glorious appearing, without shame, suffering, or death.

There it was! The reason one can be secure in the family of God — secure in the relationship of being His child: because of the completed "work of redemption" which Jesus finished on the cross and because of His death and resurrection, not because I obey or disobey or keep certain rules. No, not by anything I did to deserve or earn the status of sonship, but because God loved me and gave Himself for me.

All of that makes my being a Christian a real gift, planned before the foundation of the world. The first chapter of Ephesians (see

Living Bible paraphrase) makes this so clear
that I read and reread it in wonder and
amazement.

The way I once understood it, you would
think that eternal life was dependent totally on
what I experienced: For God so loved the
world, that He gave His only begotten Son,
that whosoever gets saved or born again shall not
perish, but have everlasting life. Actually, it
reads like this:

> *that whosoever believeth in him should not
> perish, but have everlasting life.*
>
> — KJV

What, then, does it mean to "believe in
Christ"? As briefly as I can state it, it means a
belief/trust of the emotions, the mind, and the
will about *Who He is* (His deity) and *what
He did* (His Atonement).

I began to realize that all my life I had put
the emphasis on *the what* (as it related to me
subjectively). Not until I began to accept God's
revelation, through study and meditation,
regarding the deity of Christ, *who He is,* did
the whole subject of redemption begin to fit
together and become alive.

The Chicago Visit

At the close of one spring college term,
I had to go through Chicago on my way to Seattle
where members of my family now lived. I had
decided earlier that at the first opportunity
I would hear some positive teaching on
sanctification from the "other side." Then I
heard about Founders' Week at Moody Bible

Institute, and the dates were right for me
to stop for two days.

I walked into that auditorium, picked up a
program, found a seat, and read the day's events.
I decided I would take in everything and see
for myself what these people were like. Nobody
spoke to me, nor did I venture to speak to
anyone, but I watched like a hawk. I saw, heard,
and felt everything.

I especially remember Dr. Carl Armerding
and the gentle Spirit-filled teaching he gave.
There was a study on the entire book of
Ephesians during the morning hours. In our
denomination we had never once studied the
whole book of Ephesians at a conference. I soon
discovered why: there were too many
controversial verses from our point of view.

Were these people spiritual? That was an
important test for one from my background.
It meant: Were they worldly Christians? Were
they separated from the world? I noticed that the
women were not as plain and colorless as the
women in our churches. They were more
attractively dressed, but in good taste. Some
even wore red dresses — and jewelry too! (At that
time I had never even worn a string of beads.)

They looked nice. Even their faces were
beautiful. They looked quiet, happy, and
peaceful. I couldn't see anything heretical in their
behavior or attitudes either. (What does heresy
look like anyway?)

I listened to their prayers and songs, and
most of them were just like ours.

What was the difference then?

Through all I heard, the Good News ran like
a crimson cord, for I was hearing with new ears.
I was hearing that God's love and the family

relationship are not earned by obedience, but are gifts of faith. They are forever — now and through eternity. A new security was coming through to me: that of a child born into the family, planned for, loved, and accepted.

But inner freedom to change outward standards came very slowly. Being governed by rules in a book and having them preached to you week after week results in continual immaturity. To become mature a person must develop, by personal experience, his power to discriminate between what is good and bad for him. Teaching discernment is teaching a person to think: not forcing agreement to opinion, but permitting him to learn through the choices (and mistakes) he makes. To experience the freedom Jesus promised to those who follow Him, each Christian must be convinced in his own heart as to the meaning of pleasing God and loving his brother. And this wisdom is a gift from the Holy Spirit within us.

I continued to read Paul's letter to the Ephesians in every translation I could find. It was all there: God's eternal love and plan; Christ, the Cross, the Resurrection. It was finished — forever. I am His and He is mine.

And more and more I began to realize that being a Christian is a love relationship.

John 10: the Shepherd and the sheep.

John 15: the Vine and the branches.

1 Corinthians 12: the Head and the body with all its members.

Ephesians 2:19-22; 1 Peter 2:5: the whole structure of the household of God, each one of us being bricks in the temple of God.

How can mere words ever express the excitement I felt in discovering God's full plan!

My place in the family; my place as one of
His sheep; my place among the bricks of the
temple; my place as a member of His body.

Would He ever cut me off? Disinherit me?
Pull out that brick and discard it? Leave the
sheep lost and alone? In my right mind I couldn't
conceive of Him doing such a thing — nor
would I do it to myself. How could He, then, who
is greater than I, let anything separate me from
Himself? My concept of *His greatness* was
growing by leaps and bounds.

I stopped fighting the whole idea and
embraced it, unanswered questions included.
After all, even the greatest among us do not have
all the answers. But, thank God, He gives us
enough to bring rest to the inner spirit.

The remainder can wait. . . .

Until the day when God reveals it all to us.

Chapter 12

I pray for them. . . .
O holy Father! Keep them safe
by the power of your name,
the name you gave me,
so they may be one
just as you and I are one. . . .
I made you known to them and
I will continue to do so,
in order that the love
you have for me
may be in them, and
I may be in them.

John 17:9, 11, 26
Good News for Modern Man

LOVE WITHIN THE CIRCLE

This is my commandment:
love one another, just as I love you.

— John 15:12,
Good News for Modern Man

Do I think these two schools of thought I've written about in this book will ever get together in agreement on what the Scriptures teach?

God does not say "agree with one another in order that you may love one another." But He clearly commands; "Love one another, just as I love you." In other words, we are called on to exercise, by use and by action, the Royal Law of Love, the term James uses (2:8, KJV).
This love is the greatest force in the world.

We are told to love our neighbor and not to judge him, but to leave him to the tender mercies of our Father-God. We cannot sit on the lover's seat and the judge's seat at the same time.

Love is the evidence of the Holy Spirit within us. The Holy Spirit, the Comforter, is the resurrected Jesus come back to be with us and within us forever. In union with Him and with each other "the whole body grows and builds itself up through love" (Eph. 4:16, GNMM).

Why, then, are there so many dissenting believers in Christendom?

First, we have to reckon with the stubbornness of man to hold to his taught religious beliefs and avoid thinking them out for himself. Men have died for their beliefs, and they will die for them again. Men have tortured and killed each other for refusal to change a religious viewpoint.

Second, although the human heart longs for oneness, love, and understanding, the heart is idealistic to the nth degree — even to its own undoing. It refuses to accept anything less than totality, especially in the Christian life and walk. Not understanding the difference between Law and Love results in a backlog of real and false guilt for oneself and judgment without love for our brother.

Third, religious prejudice, being void of brotherly love, springs from lack of contact with persons on the other side, as well as lack of adequate knowledge of the Scriptures.

Fourth, there is failure to realize that God is on both sides and that His purpose is to unite all things in Christ (Col. 1:20). He starts with people who are His, giving them the father-child relationship by baptizing them with His own Spirit. Read 1 Corinthians 12:12-31 which continues right on into the love chapter, 1 Corinthians 13.

If we abandon the word "sides" and use a circle for our illustration, it will help us, for God does not take sides. He is Truth. The circle is a symbol of union. To be in union with Christ means to be living our lives "within" Him or with Him. Or to change the wording, let Him live out His life from within us.

The first time I read Ephesians in the *Good News for Modern Man* translation, the impact was tremendous. The key phrase of Ephesians is "in Christ." *Good News* translates it "in union with Christ." It all ties in with the practical story of the little Chinese woman in whom Christ lived.

And finally, the great high-priestly prayer of our Lord in John 17 is still in the process of being answered. Jesus prayed in the will of His Father; consequently, His prayer for the unity of His people will be answered. It is being answered today in the great charismatic revival which is sweeping Protestant and Catholic churches alike.

What kind of unity? What kind of love?

That oneness which is loving without total agreement. The oneness which is a miracle gift from God.

When will God's children become one?

It may well be in the next world, but some of us whose eyes are being opened are making our start now. It could be when we personally allow the prayer of our Lord to be answered in us.

When will this oneness take place?

When our oneness is centered in our Lord Jesus Christ and not in verbal agreement, legalism, or doctrine.

When we can be vulnerable enough to share our
personal experiences.
When we can be honest enough to face both the
strong and weak points in our beliefs and
admit we need each other.
When we are strong enough to trust God to help
us make our own decisions and not blindly
accept what has been handed to us.
When we will take our share of responsibility in
removing barriers and actually loving one
another, in spite of the pain of disagreement.
When we are willing to exchange judgmental
criticism for Calvary love, remembering we
are all members of the same Lord.
When we begin to realize that the younger and
weaker brothers among us need the spiritual
health which is to be found in a blending
and melding of both sides.
When we can meet in prayer and fellowship
around our Lord and His table.
When we can thus share God's releasing power in
our human predicament, we will be loving
one another.
When we begin to act on the truth given to us
in 2 Corinthians 4:7:

*We have this treasure (God in us) in earthen
vessels, that the excellency of the power may be
of God, and not of us.*
— KJV

Chapter 13

Love is a feeling to be learned.
It is gladness and it is pain.
There is not one without the other.
Love and suffering do not exclude each other.
Rather they condition each other.
Suffering transforms love to a new dimension.

Walter Trobisch
Love

LIVING WITHIN THE CIRCLE

Love is a gift from God to us
through His indwelling Spirit.

To live with the truth, *Christ in me,* means
I must maintain three viewpoints: First, to see
myself as I am; second, to see myself as God
sees me; third, to see you as God sees you.

First: I accept myself as being a member of
the human race, subject to all that attacks and
hurts a human spirit and body. I am supposed
to feel my inability and my need for a Savior.
As Norman Grubb points out, having "this
treasure in earthen vessels," we can be cleansed
from our sins, but we can't be cleansed from
feeling human. We still need to learn the right
and wrong use of "the new man" within us —
Christ in us. When we fail and fall — that's we,

not He — we do not give up; we get up, confess, accept His cleansing, and go on.

Second: Here is how God sees me, now and forever.

> . . . *through the death on the cross . . .*
> *Christ has brought you*
> *into the very presence of God,*
> *and you are standing there before him*
> *with nothing left against you —*
> *nothing left that he could even chide you for.*
> . . . *in order to bring you,*
> *holy and pure and innocent,*
> *into his presence.*
>
> — Colossians 1:22,
> *Living Bible, Good News for Modern Man*

God's supply of grace, cleansing, and love existed long before our need became apparent. In His eyes, the whole process has already been completed.

I'll admit that the existing paradox of being faulty and being perfect sometimes disturbs me, but having had my fill of the other possibilities (no sinning, dying to sin, rationalization), I find more possibility in the teaching of growth through conflict. His presence with me and within me is a fact, like my right hand is a fact.

Third: Seeing others as God sees them, perfect in Christ, is a truth to be counted on not only individually, but collectively as we minister to and help one another in love. For we are members of His body living within the circle of His love.

An illustration of how this principle works came to me recently when I received a phone call from Denise, my sister in Seattle. I had completely forgotten the whole incident until this conversation brought it to mind again.

"Last week at our Bible Study Fellowship a woman asked me when Ros was coming back for a visit. She told me that a contact with you resulted in her whole life being changed. After hearing you talk, she requested that you pray for her daughter. Before you did, you prayed for her personally, asking God to heal her cold, to pour His love into her and heal any hurt places. Then you prayed for her daughter. God answered those prayers. But it was the fact that you cared about *her*, touched *her*, put your arm around *her* as you prayed that broke her up. She has been praying for and with others ever since that happened. A whole new ministry has been given to her."

This is the ministry of love which God through the Spirit of Christ gives us for one another. Just as the branches live in and bear fruit for the vine, so is the relationship between God and His children: it is a love relationship (John 15:7-17).

My search for perfection and usefulness has brought me again and again to the Person of Jesus Christ. As I look back over the chapters I have written, in one sense or another they are all illustrations of how God's love came through to me or through me to others.

The Christian life is not lived alone. Problem-centered people are self-centered people. When I let Christ within me handle both my problems and myself (without answers sometimes), I find I am reaching out with love and caring toward the person nearest me at the time. Giving and receiving love in the weakness of being imperfect are doors to mental and spiritual health. We are part of what we receive when we give it away.

Teaching people to pray together was not my idea. It was given to me when I observed that by the simplicity of praying a few words of thanks to God aloud with others, love was born! God was present!

People love each other when they begin to pray with each other, for the miracle of acceptance begins there in the presence of God, within the circle of His love.

> *Each one of us has been given*
> *a special gift. . . .*
> *to build up the body of Christ.*
> *And so we shall all come together*
> *to that oneness*
> *in our faith and in our knowledge*
> *of the Son of God;*
> *we shall become mature men. . . .*
> *speaking the truth in a spirit of love,*
> *we must grow up in every way*
> *to Christ, who is the head.*
>
> *Under his control all the different*
> *parts of the body fit together,*
> *and the whole body*
> *is held together by every joint*
> *with which it is provided.*
> *So when each separate part works*
> *as it should,*
> *the whole body grows and*
> *builds itself up through love.*
>
> — Ephesians 4:7-16,
> *Good News for Modern Man*

BIBLIOGRAPHY AND
RECOMMENDED READING

Books read during this writing or recommended for further reading.

Bennett, Dennis J., *Nine O'Clock in the Morning,* Logos, 1970.

Caldwell, Taylor, *Great Lion of God,* Doubleday, 1970.

Elliot, Elisabeth, *The Liberty of Obedience,* Word, 1968

Gilmore, G. Don, *Freedom to Fail,* Revell, 1966.

Greeley, Andrew, *The Friendship Game,* Doubleday, 1970.

Grossman, Siegfried, *Charisma: The Gifts of the Spirit,* Key Publishers, 1971.

Grubb, Norman, *God Unlimited,* Christian Literature Crusade, 1962.

Grubb, Norman, *The Spontaneous You,* Christian Literature Crusade, 1970.

Ironside, H. A., *Holiness: The False and the True,* Loizeaux, 1912.

Jones, E. Stanley, *Victory Through Surrender,*
   Abingdon, 1966.
Kunkel, Fritz, *In Search of Maturity,* Scribner, 1943.
Mollenkott, Virginia E., *In Search of Balance,*
   Word, 1969.
Powell, John, *Why am i afraid to tell you who i am?,*
   Peacock Books, Argus Communications, 1969.
Powers, Thomas E., *First Questions on the Life of the
   Spirit,* Harper & Row, 1959.
Rimmer, C. Brandon and Brown, Bill, *The
   Unpredictable Wind,* Aragorn, 1972.
Tournier, Paul, *Guilt and Grace,* Harper & Row, 1962.
Tournier, Paul, *The Meaning of Persons,*
   Harper & Row, 1957.

TREVOR

Text and Illustrations by

JAMES LECESNE

Seven Stories Press

NEW YORK

First trade paperback edition August 2013.

Seven Stories Press
140 Watts Street
New York, NY 10013
www.sevenstories.com

College professors may order examination copies of Seven Stories Press titles for a free six-month trial period. To order, visit http://www.sevenstories.com/textbook or send a fax on school letterhead to (212) 226-1411.

Library of Congress Cataloging-in-Publication Data

Lecesne, James.
Trevor / James Lecesne. -- 1st ed.
    p. cm.
Summary: Bullied at school, dumped by his friends, and pressured at home, an artistic teenager struggling with his sexuality and identity makes a desperate attempt to end his loneliness.
Includes bibliographical references (p.).
ISBN 978-1-60980-420-6 (hardback) -- ISBN 978-1-60980-487-9 (pb)
[1. Sexual orientation--Fiction. 2. Sex role--Fiction. 3. Suicide--Fiction.] I. Title.
PZ7.L483Tr 2012
[Fic]--dc23
                          2012016377

Book design by Jon Gilbert

Printed in the USA

9 8 7 6 5 4 3 2 1

This book is dedicated to the memory of

Randy Stone

cofounder of The Trevor Project

CONTENTS

FOREWORD

by David Levithan

I f you've picked up this book, the odds are strong that you were a Trevor, are a Trevor, or have a Trevor in your life. All of these are good things.

I was a Trevor. Using my action figures to act out soap operas. ("Chewbacca . . . you're looking lovely this evening.") Creating elaborate ruses to avoid any contact with the physical aspects of physical education. (Far left field, c'est moi.) Listening to the top 40 countdown on the radio and watching MTV with a pop-cultural obsessiveness that would, in future generations, fuel a million blogs. And, oh yes, for everything I really, really knew about myself, there were multitudes about which I was entirely clueless.

None of this really goes away. Nor does the hurt that comes from unfairness. Or the frustration—often self-directed—that comes when the stories in your life don't quite match up to the stories in your head. But a lot of times, the things you create can compensate mightily for the things you have no control over.

I meet Trevors all the time. Kids. Teenagers. Adults. Here's what makes them wonderful: They bring things to life. They hear music. They see color. They cherish their capacity for wonder. They feel. Even when it's not easy, they feel.

The world doesn't always know what to do with Trevors. That's why those of us who are Trevors, or once were Trevors, or simply appreciate Trevors, have to do everything we can. Because it's not the Trevors who need to change. It's the world.

If this sounds too difficult—if this even seems impossible—please consider the story you now have in your hands.

Before there was Glee, before there was Ellen, before there was Lady Gaga, before there was "It Gets Better," before there was Lawrence v. Texas, before there was any gay website that you've ever visited, before there was any gay YA novel written by myself or any of my contemporaries, there was Trevor. First as a play, then as an Academy Award–winning short film, and now as a novel. And always as a boy—an amazing, confused, completely endearing boy.

You may have first heard Trevor's name as part of The Trevor Project, the phenomenal lifeline for LGBTQ teens that sprung from Trevor's story. I can think of no better example of art becoming so powerful that it actually makes a change in the world. Yes, this is how the world can work: a fictional teen based on a real teen can lead to the aid of thousands upon thousands of real teens, who will then go out and make their own creations and contributions. The beauty of this astonishes me.

It is far too easy to feel small. It is far too easy to be made to feel small. It is far too easy to feel your bigger thoughts and bigger dreams confined to the smallness around you, especially (but not only) in high school. Trevor falls into these traps, as we all do, time and time again. But what Trevor learns—what we all must learn—is that we are never small within our own lives. And the way out of the smallness around us is to reach. Not for death or negation, but for the better realms our bigger imaginations can conjure. We take hold of the music. We take hold of the color. We take hold of the wonder. And we feel our way to the greater place.

When I was a high-school Trevor, I spent a lot of time listening to Carly Simon. My anthem was a song that commanded Let all the dreamers wake the nation. Now, still a Trevor, knowing so many more Trevors, I say: let all the Trevors, and all their friends, wake the nation. The story starts here. But as James Lecesne and the Trevor Project have proven, where it goes from here holds infinite possibilities.

ONE

There I was, lying on the front lawn in plain sight with a knife in my back. Actually that was the effect I was going for, and to be perfectly honest, I think it looked pretty good—from the street. I had gone to a lot of trouble in order to create the illusion that I'd been murdered. First, I borrowed Mom's kitchen knife (the big one) and planted it firmly in the dirt. Then I positioned my body so that it looked to the people who happened to be driving by in their cars that I'd been stabbed to death. The fact that Dad was nonchalantly mowing the lawn made the whole thing seem (in my opinion) even more macabre. Imagine that you are driving past a typical suburban house on a typical suburban street in a typical suburban town somewhere in America at the beginning of the twenty-first century. A guy is mowing his lawn. You happen to turn your head and catch sight of this kid—thirteen years old, brown hair, wearing a t-shirt, jeans, and running shoes. He's lying on the grass with a knife stuck in his back. Horrors! What do you do? Do you turn your head away and pretend you didn't see it? Call 911? Stop and point out to the guy who is mowing the lawn that his kid appears to be dead? Do you stop the car, jump out, and administer mouth-to-mouth resuscitation? What?

These are a few of the questions I pondered while lying there trying to make it look like I wasn't breathing by keeping my chest and stomach perfectly still. It's hard to do, but I had been practicing this for years and eventually I developed a technique to simulate deadness. I can fool trained paramedics, which I did once when I was in seventh grade (the trained paramedic was my cousin Sara, but still). Anyway, I was doing a pretty good job of being a murder victim when I heard my Dad yell over the sound of the mower.

"WHAT?"

"MY KITCHEN KNIFE," Mom yelled back from the porch where she was standing. "HAVE YOU SEEN IT? THE BIG ONE?"

Dad did not reply, but I imagine that by this time Mom had spotted me lying there in plain sight along with her knife. I opened one eye just enough to see her marching across the front lawn. She was coming toward me, and she did not look happy. I'd say, based on her facial expression and body language, exasperation would be a more fitting description of her mental state. The fact that she was wearing an apron made me deduce that she had been in the middle of cooking dinner and then realized that her knife (the big one) was missing. After looking high and low, the logical next step would have been to ask Dad if he'd taken it from the kitchen. He is always using her kitchen utensils for inappropriate household activities like cutting tree branches or unscrewing something on his car. Once she

spotted me, I figured that I'd be receiving a good talking-to, so I shut my eyes and braced myself for her verbal onslaught.

Let me just say that Mom has never been my best audience. Ever. She has always been very busy with either housework or her job. As she often reminds me, she doesn't have the time or the energy for my "shenanigans" and she wishes to God that I would find something constructive to do with my time, something other than sitting in my room doodling for hours or lying on the front lawn pretending to be dead. What about baseball, she has asked me on more than one occasion. "Would it kill you to go over and ask that gang of boys if they needed an extra outfielder or something?" She didn't understand that in fact I *was* being constructive. I had gone to a lot of trouble in order to create the effect of my own murder on the front lawn, but unfortunately, due to her position, it was lost on her. I was really doing it for the benefit of the random people who were passing by our house. From the other angle, it must have looked as though I'd fallen asleep on the front lawn with the knife stuck in the grass beside me. I doubt she would have enjoyed having the whole thing explained to her, so I kept my mouth shut and kept on pretending to be dead. Knowing Mom, she probably was able to figure out what I was up to and just wasn't that impressed.

In any case, she reached down and quickly snatched the

knife from the lawn. Then she wheeled herself around and headed back toward the house without a word. She didn't even bother to yell at me. Maybe she thought I was doing this as a ploy to get attention, but I was just trying to keep myself entertained. It's fun to be pretend-dead and then lie there as the world goes on without you. In my opinion, this is a much better use of my time than playing baseball.

The mower started up again, but I could hear Dad's voice shouting over the sound of the revving motor.

"TREVOR," he yelled. "GET UP. I HAVE TO FINISH THE LAWN AND YOU'RE IN THE WAY . . . TREVOR!"

TWO

I don't want to give you the impression that Mom and Dad are uncaring people who are insensitive to my needs; they are merely busy. Mom works as an administrator processing applications for insurance claims—or something like that—at the local hospital. Dad is a regional manager for a company that distributes products designed to make things that stick, like tape and industrial-strength glue. As an artist, I am not exactly inspired by the type of work they do, but I totally appreciate the fact that ever since I can remember they have kept a roof over my head and sent me to school fed and fully dressed. As their only child, I have always had pretty much everything I need. We are not rich by any means. I guess you could say that we are comfortably well off. Mom and Dad are tired at the end of the day—the result of their hard work—and they like to relax in the evening by parking themselves in front of the TV and watching some dumb game show or a televised talent contest in which people are pitted against one another until one of them wins a chance to be recognized by strangers in shopping malls across the country.

One night, while they were watching TV, I walked into the living room and fell dead to the floor. I held my breath a good long time. No response from them. That was when I decided that their ability to spontaneously respond to their environment (and me) had been compromised by the television. Unless I happened to be dancing with a star, I don't think they would notice me—and I have never danced with a star in my whole life.

Sometimes instead of hanging around in my room surfing the net, drawing, or just being ignored to death by my parents, I sneak out of the house and go over to Zac's house, which is just four blocks away. Zac and I have been friends since second grade, but now that we're in high school and we don't do kid stuff anymore, we have been working on more grown-up activities. For example, one night Zac asked me if I wanted to come over and check out his new microscope. I said yes, hopped on my bike, and went upstairs to his room without his parents knowing what was up. And wow! Let me tell you, we saw a lot of crazy activity through the eyepiece of that microscope. His sperm was amazing! Zac said that people used to think masturbating could cause a person to go totally deaf. Apparently he had read all about this and, according to the Internet, it was something they told to young boys in order to get them to stop "abusing" themselves.

"I am no expert," I told Zac, "but I've never heard of a single case where someone went deaf due to masturbation."

"What'd you say?!" Zac asked, pretending to be deaf.

We had big laugh over that one.

Then things got ugly.

He asked me if I was planning to dress up for Halloween, and I told him that I was considering going as Lady Gaga.

"Why?" he asked, and I could tell that he disapproved of my idea.

I explained to him that Lady Gaga was (a) my absolute fave, (b) an icon, and (c) an original who knew how to

upend people's expectations of normalcy. He wasn't convinced, and announced that he was going to be a superhero
for Halloween. He suggested that I join him, or at the very
least consider something "less gay." I informed him that
Lady Gaga was certainly not gay.

"You're missing the whole point," he told me.

Before he could say anything further, I jumped in: "No,
Zac, *you're* missing the point. Because anyone who knows
anything about Lady Gaga knows that she has had to over-
come plenty of obstacles to become the artist that she is
today. And in order to be myself and achieve my goals, I
will have to do the same."

He rolled his eyes and said, "Whatever."

End of discussion.

After that I was even more determined than ever to be
the most awesome, gender-bending version of Lady Gaga
for Halloween. Mom dropped me at the mall, and with my
birthday money, I purchased the following items:

One full-body leotard (black): $14.95

One wig (blond): $18.45

One sequined cape (silver): $19.99

One pair of oversize sunglasses (black): $8.00

One pair of platform slouch boots (black): $27.99

2-lb bag of glitter (silver): $10.00

TOTAL: $99.38

THREE

Last week in art history class, Mr. Livorgna explained to us how sometimes great art can be both a reaction to the politics of the moment and an enduring statement about the human condition. To prove his point, he pulled up some famous paintings on his laptop. He showed us a mostly black-and-white painting of crudely drawn people and animals—they all seemed to be suffering violently. A horse, a bull, a baby, and a person lying on the ground stretching out his hand for help. To us, it looked like a gruesome mess drawn by a fifth-grader. Mr. Livorgna explained that the artist was, in fact, Picasso and that gruesome was the whole point. *Guernica* (that's the name of the painting) was created to show the tragedies of war and the suffering it inflicts upon individuals, particularly innocent civilians. He said the work gained a monumental status right from the start, becoming famous and widely acclaimed when it was displayed around the world. Incidentally, he said, this tour helped bring the Spanish Civil War to the world's attention. Who knew that Spain even had a Civil War?

"Can you think of any other examples of how artists have brought about change through their work?" he asked us.

Silence.

I almost raised my hand to mention how Lady Gaga had famously worn a suit made entirely of meat in order to protest the fact that gays in the military had to keep their sexuality a secret or else be kicked out with a dishonorable discharge. But then I thought better of it. I didn't want everyone to think that I followed gay news. Besides I couldn't say for sure whether Lady Gaga's meat-suit media moment actually brought an end to the policy the army called "Don't Ask, Don't Tell." The fact that this policy existed for seventeen years but was overturned by Congress just a couple of months after she wore the suit wasn't proof of anything. Some people said that Lady Gaga was just an opportunist who was using the politics of the moment to further her career. Some said she was an activist. I wondered if Picasso had the same trouble with *Guernica*.

When no one could come up with any examples, Mr. Livorgna clicked on to the next image, and started to describe a painting entitled *La Mort de Marat*, which is French for *The Death of Marat*. The style of this painting was much more realistic and it depicted a man who had been stabbed in his bathtub while writing a letter. It was very dramatic, and the guy was obviously very dead. Little spurts of blood stained some sheets that spilled out of the tub; he was wearing a white turban and held a feather pen in his right hand, which had dropped dramatically to the floor at the moment of his murder. Mr. Livorgna told us that this was one of the most famous images of the French Revolution, and it referred to the assassination of a radical journalist named Jean-Paul Marat.

When I got home I Googled the image and read all about Monsieur Marat. Not only was he a journalist, but he was also a doctor, a statesman, and a great public speaker. I don't know why, but I became fascinated by this image and the story of how Jean-Paul had been killed in his bathtub by a French revolutionary named Charlotte Corday. Perhaps it reminded me that anything could happen to any one of us at any moment. Our lives could change—or end—with a moment's notice.

For my art history extra credit project I decided to recreate the scene from *La Mort de Marat*. An artist that Mr. Livorgna visually introduced us to the week before had inspired me. Her name was Cindy Sherman, and starting in the 1970s she began to make a name for herself by being photographed in the guises of random people. My plan was to take a picture of myself in the bath in the pose of poor old Marat, and then

maybe be discovered as the youngest artist of my generation. I got a hold of my mother's terry-cloth shower turban,
I found an old quill pen that I had purchased years ago when
I went to Philadelphia on a school trip to view the actual
Declaration of Independence, and I bought a packet of fake
blood from the Halloween section of the local card shop. I
was all set and super excited. After applying the blood to my
body and the sheet, I sat in the bathtub and tried to imagine

what it must have felt like to be murdered by a revolutionary who was brave (or crazy) enough to come to where I live and stab me in my bath.

Unfortunately, I was interrupted by the sound of my mother pulling back the shower curtain and then turning on the faucet. Before I knew what was happening, a steady stream of cold water had extinguished my French Revolutionary fantasy, and any chance of extra credit went swirling down the drain.

"Clean up this mess," said Mom, as she presented me with a wet sponge mop.

What Mom failed to understand was that, just like Lady Gaga, I refused to be discouraged from becoming an artist or expressing my true self in an artistic way. And just like Lady Gaga, I intended to change the world.

FOUR

"What's wrong?" Mom asked me.

I was pushing my breakfast burrito around on my plate, not exactly eating, but not exactly not eating either.

"Nothing," I told her.

She wasn't convinced.

"Why don't you invite Zac over after school and play a board game? Wouldn't that be fun?"

A board game? I haven't played a board game since I was in fourth grade. Sometimes Mom can be so retro. Hasn't she heard of computers? The Internet? Facebook?

"You mean, a *bored* game?" I asked her, without looking up from my plate.

Mom shook her head, downed the rest of her coffee, and went about her business. What I couldn't tell her was that Zac and I were no longer friends; he had stopped returning my calls, and when I passed him in the hallway at school, he kind of totally brushed me off. Finally I confronted him at his locker, saying, "What's up?"

He responded by looking around and saying in a voice that was louder than necessary: "Well, if it isn't Lady Gay-Gay."

As a result of that experience, I made a decision to expand my social horizons and accept an invitation to hang out with a gang of kids I hardly knew. Katie Quinn said it would be cool for me to join her and her posse after school because they were planning to hang out at the Quality Courts Motel, and another body wouldn't make any difference one way or the other.

"Cool," I said in response.

I didn't know what to expect, but what I discovered was that the motel hadn't actually been completed; it was just a construction site at the far end of town with a "COMING SOON" sign. We all scaled the fence, boys and girls together, and then once inside the structure, we checked the place out, wandering from floor to floor and calling to one another like idiots. Eventually, someone yelled that they'd found a few habitable rooms, and one of the guys declared that these rooms would be our new clubhouse until further notice.

Somehow I ended up alone in a room with Katie. Since we had nothing better to do and there was no place to sit, I suggested that we try to French-kiss. I told her that we could consider it a controlled experiment. To tell you the truth, I had no trouble controlling myself. I didn't feel anything. Maybe it was the fact that Katie has braces on her teeth, but I remember thinking: Is this what all the fuss is about? And what makes it French?

In any case, Katie and I made a date to try it again soon.

When I got home, Mom was in a state. Where had I been all this time? Why hadn't I answered my cell phone? Did I see the text messages she sent me? She sent me seven of them. Seven! She had been so worried that she was about to call the police. And what was the matter with my lips? Why were they so red and swollen?

When I explained to her that I had been kissing a girl, it was like the sun had broken through the clouds. Her face lit up, and she smiled as though she had just been awarded an all-expenses paid Caribbean cruise.

"Really?" she asked, as her eyes began to tear up. "Really and truly?"

"Really," I replied. "And truly."

"Oh, honey! This is cause for celebration!"

She did a little happy dance right there in the kitchen, hopping around like she herself had just been kissed for the first time.

"I know," she said, when she was finished dancing. "Let's call your father at work and tell him."

That night one of the boys from the motel unexpectedly

friended me on Facebook. His name was Pinky Faraday. (I know what you're thinking. You're thinking that a guy named Pinky is probably gay, right? Well, he isn't. Not in the least. Pinky is the star of the intermediate baseball team in town and everything. He is taller than me by like a foot; he has dark hair, blue eyes, and a toothy grin that he only flashes when he really means it.) When I called Katie to tell her what had happened, she told me that she thought Pinky was stuck-up and kind of moody. I told her that I thought he was deep and had a lot on his mind. As my Dad would say, we agreed to disagree.

Being Facebook friends with Pinky meant so much to me. It was a big deal and an even bigger surprise because, really, I hadn't done anything to make it happen—it had just happened. And once it happened I felt that it was the next best thing to being popular myself. But to be honest, I wasn't exactly sure why Pinky wanted to be my friend, so I invited him to meet me after school at the Coffee Connection to discuss the matter in person. Naturally, I didn't mention that we were going to discuss our friendship; I just mentioned coffee and maybe tea as options.

Pinky couldn't stay long. He said that his father was giving him and his brothers a hard time lately due to the fact that they had almost burned down the house. He said it wasn't their fault, and I believed him. But still, his father was making them do yard work after school for like a month as a kind of community service.

"How big is your yard?" I asked him, thinking that a month was a long time.

"Not big enough," was his reply.

According to Pinky, his home life wasn't exactly stable. Ever since his father remarried, the Faraday household had been in turmoil because his stepmother had very particular ideas about how they ought to be living, ideas that were far from the way they had been living for as long as anyone could remember. For example, the new Mrs. Faraday was insisting that they all sit down to dinner every night as a family. Pinky was against this sort of thing because they were not, in his opinion, a family. Just because his father had fallen in love with someone did not give that someone the right to decide the eating habits of people she hardly knew. He said that his own mother, when she was alive, allowed everyone in the family to eat when and where they wanted, and as a result holidays were always super special.

"You could count on Christmas and Thanksgiving," Pinky said as he wistfully recalled the past. "We always got together and sometimes nobody left the table for hours. Once my Dad even fell asleep right there at the dining room table and we had to wake him up the next morning for breakfast."

Pinky showed me a picture of his mother that he carried in his wallet. She was a pretty woman with dyed blond hair, blue eyes, and the same bright smile that Pinky had; in fact, her resemblance to Pinky was remarkable. When I pointed it out to him, I noticed that there were tears in his eyes. He told me that he kept a framed copy of the picture next to his bed as well to remind him where he came from.

Pinky was the coolest guy I had ever met because, though he was tough on the outside, he had real feelings and he was not afraid to show them in public. I gave him back the photograph, and we then made a date to see one another again the following week.

FIVE

The Drama Club announced auditions for the winter production of Cole Porter's *Anything Goes*. This is a musical extravaganza featuring plenty of madcap antics aboard an ocean liner bound from New York to London. The score includes such hit songs as "Anything Goes," "You're the Top," and "I Get a Kick Out of You." Of course these were hit songs back in the twentieth century before there was radio, and as a result teenagers today are not as familiar with the work of Cole Porter as they are with, say, Lady Gaga. When I asked Pinky, for instance, if perhaps he and a few of the guys might be interested in trying out for the chorus of *Anything Goes*, he responded by saying, "What's that?" After explaining the plot as well as the process of auditioning for musical theater, everyone including Pinky said that they weren't too interested.

"Sounds gay," said one of the guys.

And that, I thought, was that.

But then the following day, word got around that Tanya Handley had snagged the lead part of Reno Sweeney, an evangelist turned nightclub singer. Tanya put out an unofficial challenge, saying that if any "real men" showed up to audition for the part opposite her, she would personally kiss them on the lips. Pinky and a few of the guys took up the challenge and, though none of them were talented enough to play either the part of Lord Evelyn Oakleigh or Public Enemy #13 Moonface Martin, all of them did get an opportunity to make out with Tanya in the stairwell. Later, when the cast list was posted in the band room, I was super excited (but not surprised) to get the part of Lord Oakleigh. But my thrill was soon multiplied when I learned that Pinky and the guys had all been cast in the chorus.

"Personally," Katie remarked, "I think it's just the idea of being close to Tanya that's getting those guys all worked up."

I told Katie that that was totally understandable due to the fact that Tanya had star quality, and the responsibility of a star is to make everyone feel more excited about everything when she is around. In other words, Tanya was just doing her job, and also Katie was jealous that she hadn't been cast in a lead part.

Since I had been responsible for getting Pinky and his gang to (a) show up and (b) audition, both Katie and Tanya considered me the go-to-guy, and they invited me to take the helm and direct the entire production. My reaction was so over-the-top that Ms. Potter, the teaching supervisor of the Drama Club, had to take several steps back to avoid injury. Once I was finished reacting to the news, I assured everyone present that not only would I consider the job, I would take it and run with it! They would not be disappointed. As I walked away, I remember thinking: life just doesn't get any better than this.

After a week of play practice, I began to realize that this was a bigger challenge than I had thought. Though each day the guys got better and better, they couldn't seem to learn the dance steps that I'd been teaching them, and they had yet to sing a single lyric. It seemed that they could only concentrate on their movements if they were completely silent and stared at their feet, and even then the choreography was a train wreck every time. Nevertheless, I was determined that by opening night they would be good!

One evening after play practice, Pinky and I were walking home together and I explained once again the concept of musical theater by demonstrating the dance steps while singing the lyrics. The air was crisp and cold, and the sky was like a deep blue dream of heaven. I think for the first time in my life I was totally and truly happy. The two of us just ambled along the sidewalks, occasionally stopping to review a dance move or talk about our future. Pinky said that he

was thinking of quitting the show because he didn't consider himself musical comedy material and also rehearsals were interfering with his basketball practice. I told him that one of the first things we learned in the theater as young thespians was that the show must go on. It must.

"How come?" he asked me.

"I don't know," I told him. "It just has to."

The minute I said this, I knew that my mind was made up. My future had been decided, and I had to tell someone.

"Hey," I said to Pinky as we stopped on the pavement. "Can I tell you something that I have never ever told another living soul in my whole life?"

"Sure."

"I have decided that the theater is to be my life."

"Cool," Pinky replied, and he started walking again.

Pinky was so understanding, and all the way home he encouraged me totally in the pursuit of my dream. Even though he didn't have a lick of experience in the field of entertainment, he told me that he could recognize talent when he saw it and, as far as he was concerned, I definitely had whatever was necessary to become a big success. Then he added that anyone with half a brain could see that someone with my kind of passion was going to go very far in this world.

Pinky made it home in time for dinner. But before he went inside the house, he told me that I was special and he wondered why he never noticed me before. He was standing under a streetlight, looking like a superhero. As I walked away, I thought to myself, if someone came to town with a machine gun and threatened to kill Pinky, I'd offer myself instead. He definitely deserved to live.

Zac finally called. I thanked him for getting back to me, but I explained that I couldn't possibly come over. When he asked me why not, I explained how busy I was with rehearsals and all. Also, now that Pinky Faraday and I were BFFs, my schedule wasn't as open as it was when I was in, say, fourth grade. When I wasn't rehearsing, I sometimes went down to watch Pinky shoot hoops, and occasionally Pinky and I met for a hot drink at the Coffee Connection.

Zac told me that I ought to be careful.

"Careful?" I said. "Of what?"

"Of becoming a gay," he answered. "Boys doing it with boys is totally gross, and you can end up a pervert. Or worse."

"Zac?" I said into the phone. "Are you jealous?"

"Don't be a dickhead, dickhead" he said, snarkily. "I'm just saying that up until like yesterday that Pinky kid was totally ignoring you. Now you're like best friends? I just don't like it, that's all."

Zac has always been a big complainer. His specialty is complaining about how people are always treating us as though we're invisible. Some of his favorite comments are:

1) *They didn't even say hello!*

2) *That girl looked right through me!*

3) *Are they just going to pretend we don't exist? HEL-LO?*

Whenever Zac gets like this I explain to him that rather than waiting around for others to say hello or notice him, he'd be much better off DOING something in order to distinguish himself. "You need to make people take notice of you," I tell him. "You need to stand up in order to stand out."

"Right," he said with plenty of sulk in his voice.

"I know!" I offered. "Why don't you get involved in the chorus of *Anything Goes?*"

"You mean like singing and dancing?" he asked.

"It's not too late."

"Dude," he said, deepening his voice. "That is so gay."

SIX

The show went on without a hitch. Tanya was brilliant and her rendition of "Anything Goes" got a standing ovation at both performances. Jed Steckler came down with a wicked case of flu and as a result the audiences never got to enjoy his hilarious portrayal of Public Enemy #13 Moonface Martin. Instead I had to step in at the last moment and double as both Moonface and Lord Oakleigh. It was exhausting—and terrifying. But people came up to me afterwards to tell me that they were utterly amazed, not only because I could play both parts so adroitly and make all of the quick changes, but also because in scenes where both characters appeared, I was able to slip seamlessly between the two without losing my place or my footing. A tour de force, they called it. I was pretty proud.

It turned out to be a good thing that Pinky had dropped out of the show. If he had remained in the chorus, he would have been changing his costume backstage while I did my shtick onstage, and he never would have had the chance to see my performance from out in the auditorium. Besides, after two weeks of rehearsal it didn't seem as though he was ever going to get the dance steps down and do them in a convincing or artistically pleasing manner. I looked for him afterwards, but I totally understood why he didn't hang around. He had said on more than one occasion that he had already endured plenty of the cast's barbed musical-comedy comments and self-congratulatory looks. Everyone was pissed at him for dropping out at the last minute, everyone except for Tanya and me. However, he did call me at home after our cast party to tell me what he thought of the show.

"You are the real star, man."

"But what about Tanya?" I asked him as I was removing my makeup.

"Screw Tanya," he replied bitterly. "She's a stuck-up bitch who thinks too much of herself for her own good."

I couldn't believe my ears; I was so touched. He really thought I was better than Tanya!

He went on to tell me that the situation at home was not good. Apparently his father had been on a rampage for the past twenty-four hours; he had turned the Faraday household upside down—literally. I didn't want to pry, but I did ask him if he was safe. He told me that he was for the time being because he was calling me from the crawl-space up in the attic and that was why he had to whisper. "If anything happened to you, Pinky," I said, trying to hold back my tears, "I wouldn't be able to go on. I really wouldn't."

"Yes, you would," he said. "You'd be surprised how quickly people get over even the worst stuff."

A chill went up my spine because at that moment I realized that I was going to have to prove to Pinky that he was a person worth not getting over quickly.

"No," I told him. "I wouldn't."

And then very quietly, so that his father wouldn't hear him, we sang a few bars of the song "Anything Goes" together.

> *The world has gone mad today*
> *And good's bad today,*
> *And black's white today,*
> *And day's night today,*
> *When most guys today*
> *That women prize today*
> *Are just silly gigolos*
> *And though I'm not a great romancer*
> *I know that I'm bound to answer*
> *When you propose,*
> *Anything goes.*

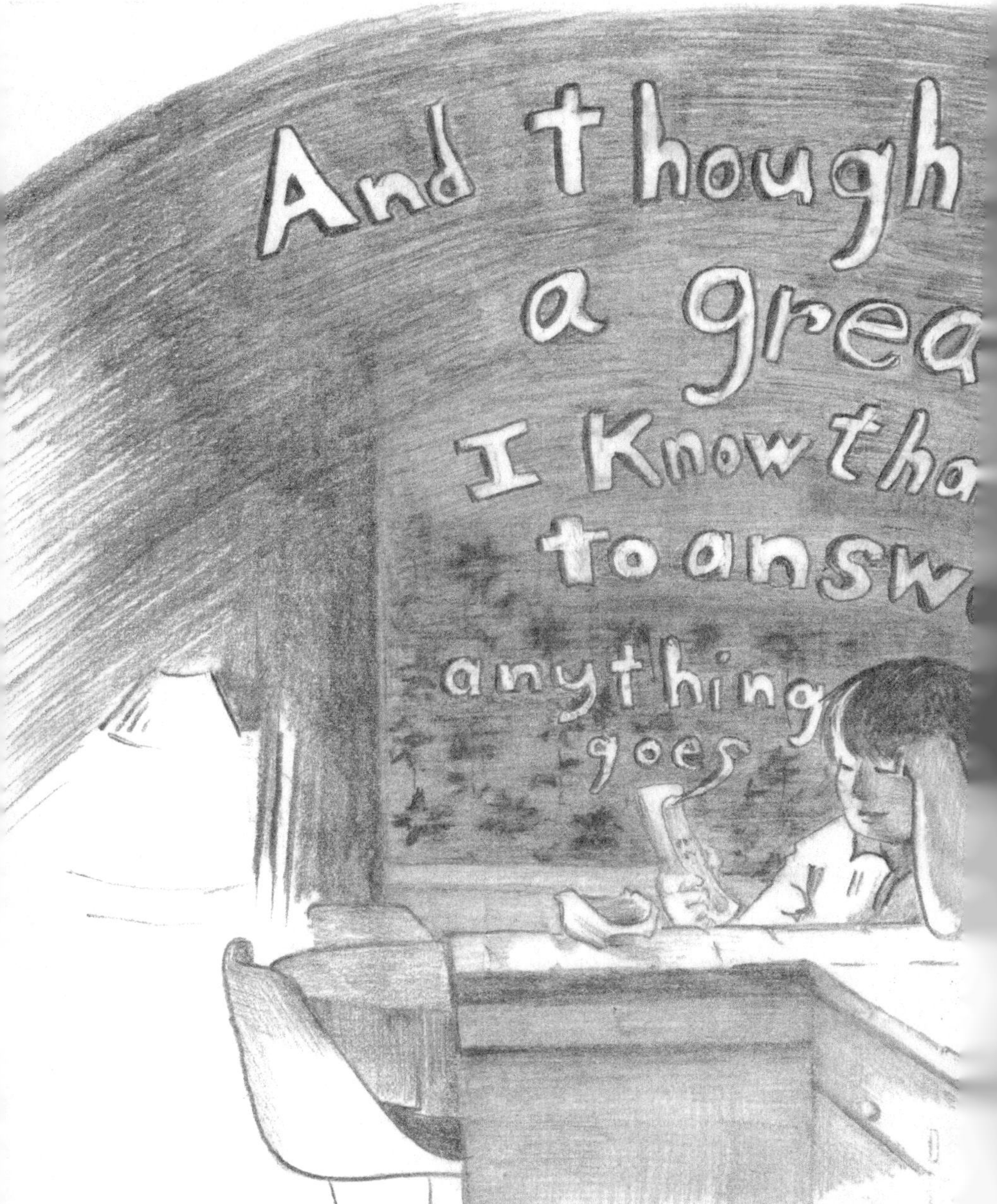

And though
a grea
I Know tha
to answ
anything
goes

'm not
romancer
I'm bound
when you propose

The next night, I called Pinky on his cell to make sure he was okay and that his father hadn't done anything crazy. When I got no response I texted him several times, sent him a message on Facebook, and then finally called his home phone. His stepmother answered. She was super polite with me, but firm. She said Pinky couldn't speak to me, and I should not try contacting him anymore. I was so stunned I didn't even ask her why. I just said "Okay" and then I hung up.

I sat down and wrote Pinky a long letter telling him what had happened, because I knew he knew nothing about it and was probably being held hostage by his father or something. I hardly slept all night.

The next day at school, I gave Pinky the letter. He took it from me without saying anything and then acted as though he was late for class, which he was not because the bell hadn't even rung yet.

At lunch, he gave me a letter back; it was written on lined paper that had been torn from a spiral notebook and though the writing was nearly illegible, I could make out every word. It said that I was a fairy, a weak person and maybe didn't even deserve to live.

This was devastating news. The worst part of it was that I felt so utterly alone. There was no one in whom I could confide. Katie and Zac had always been jealous of my friendship with Pinky, and they probably would celebrate the fact

that Pinky was finally out of the picture. Dad was away on business, and besides, he wouldn't have understood the problem. And Mom? She would have told me that maybe Pinky wasn't as good a friend as I had thought he was and then suggested that I put the whole thing behind me, call up Zac, and invite him for a sleepover like old times. How could I have told her what was really in my heart? What could she have said if I told her that I didn't want old times or that I wanted Pinky? What nobody could understand, what I could hardly understand myself, was that the one person I wanted to talk to about all this was Pinky. And that just wasn't going to happen. I couldn't exactly walk up to him at school and ask him the one thing I was dying to know—did this mean that he and I were not best friends anymore? Is that what he was trying to tell me? What had I done wrong?

SEVEN

I broke down and told Katie Quinn what happened between Pinky and me, which is to say that I told her that I didn't know what happened between Pinky and me or why he had stopped talking to me. She mentioned that she overheard some of his friends talking about me behind my back.

"What'd they say?" I asked her.

"I shouldn't say,"

"Tell me," I pleaded. "I should know."

"You don't want to know."

"Katie, please. Whatever they said can't be worse than what I'm imagining in my head right now."

"Okay. So the guys were saying you walk like a girl."

Let me just say that this was so much worse than anything that I could have ever imagined in my head. In fact, I felt as though I could have killed myself over this. Naturally, I denied it. I told Katie that I did not walk anything like a girl. I did not! She gave me a sad smile, and then I heard myself saying, "Wait. Do *you* think I walk like a girl?"

"No," was her response, "of course not."

I suggested that the best way to prove that we were both right was to give her a demonstration. Bad move. When I was finished, I turned around and I could tell by the look on her face that something was wrong.

"What?" I asked her.

"Nothing."

I went straight home and threw out my black leotard and sequined cape and all of my glitter makeup. No way was I ever going to dress up as Lady Gaga ever again. That phase of my life was over.

After that I decided to spend some time doing push-ups and also sitting in front of the mirror in my room taking a good hard look at myself. Something was wrong with me and it was definitely showing. But what? No matter how long I stood there in front of the mirror, no matter how hard I stared at my own reflection, I couldn't see the thing that was making me seem different from everybody else. My life had become an obvious tragedy; ironic that I was the only person who couldn't see it.

The next day at school Pinky stopped saying *hey* to me in between classes, and he seemed to be going out of his way to avoid me in the cafeteria. English class was a particular kind of torture because I was forced to see him for forty minutes, and he refused to look at me or acknowledge my existence. No one knew how deeply I suffered over this because I was determined to keep it to myself. This went on for more than a week, and the whole time I just wanted to know what had happened to my friendship with Pinky. Where did it go? What had I done to upset him? Was it because I walked like a girl? Maybe there was something I could do to make it better. But what?

Then Mr. Kienast asked me to read aloud from my report on the short story. This was like a form of torture specially designed to humiliate and embarrass me. As I made my way to the front of the class, I could hear the kids whispering behind my back. *That's the kid who has a crush on Pinky Faraday.* This was the longest walk I had ever taken in my life. I stood there facing the class with my stupid paper, and even though I knew it wasn't possible, I hoped that maybe this was all just a bad dream. When I realized that it wasn't a bad dream, I hoped instead that I might drop dead in front of the entire class. When that didn't happen, I swallowed hard and began.

"I chose for my topic *The Loss of Innocence as Reflected in Literature*. Here's what I wrote:

"The loss of innocence is brought about because of an experience with no explanation. The character must be involved in the experience and must experience the loss. Must be hurt. Must survive. The experience must be potent enough to be remembered and must create a subtle change in the character . . ."

Mr. Kienast gave me an A for my report. No one could tell that I copied it all from a book. Pinky continued to ignore me, and for the rest of the day I was officially invisible.

EIGHT

Mom was cleaning my room, and she just *happened* to read something that I'd been typing on my computer, a confidential email that I could have sent to my BFF—if I'd had a BFF. But since I do not have a BFF, or even a close friend in whom I could confide my deepest and most intimate feelings, the email was just idling on my screen unread—until Mom came along.

She had a fit and then we had an all-out fight. I told her that my private life was none of her business and maybe I was crazy but it seemed to me that I ought to be able to have the freedom to express my own private thoughts in the privacy of my own room and on my own "personal" computer. She claimed that I was still too young to have any kind of a life that didn't concern her, personal, private, or otherwise.

"I'm your mother," she said louder than was absolutely

necessary. "And in case you haven't noticed, I am in charge of your life."

To express my opposition to this extremely unfair point of view and to protest against people feeling that they had the right to read emails without the say-so of the person who wrote them, I attempted to run away to San Francisco. I did not leave a note. I simply packed a bag and snuck out through the garage. Unfortunately, I only got as far as the bus station. Mom dragged me back home so that she could tell me that she was very, very, very worried about me (she used three *very*'s). She sat me down in the living room and announced that we needed to have a talk.

"A talk?" I said.

"Yes," she replied. "For example, do you think you might be depressed?"

"Um," I remarked. "I'm not sure. I don't think so."

She then went on to explain that depression can often go undetected, but if left untreated it could become a serious problem in the life of a teen. Apparently, drug abuse and self-loathing are possible next steps when depression is involved—and worse.

"Worse?"

She didn't care to elaborate. Instead she told me that she couldn't even begin to imagine what it must be like for me to be a teenager living in the modern world. When she was my age, the world was an entirely different place and there were no such things as the Internet or Facebook or cell phones or texting or tweeting, and computers hadn't even been invented yet.

"But how did you communicate with your friends?" I asked her.

"By speaking to them," she replied. "Either face-to-face or on the telephone."

She explained that when she was growing up, they only had one telephone and it was located in the hallway of the house. Her sisters, her mother and father, everyone knew all about her business. And though at the time she resented the fact that she was not allowed to have secrets, she had come to realize that her family was able to help her simply because they always knew what she was going through.

"So that's why I was wondering," Mom said. "Are you going through something I should know about?"

When I didn't respond, she pulled out my art history notebook, opened it, and showed me the inside cover. There, alongside a pencil sketch of some random fruits and an earthenware jug, Pinky's name was doodled in script. Each letter was carefully shaded and colored. Then she slowly turned the pages, showing me other examples of Pinky's name written over and over in all the margins.

"That's Katie's notebook," I blurted out. "She loaned it to me. It's not mine, if that's what you're thinking."

Mom's shoulders dropped and she let out a sigh of either

defeat or relief. As she stood up, she handed me the note-book and said: "Well, let's make sure that Katie gets it back."

And then to signal that our talk was over, she leaned over and took me in her arms. She hugged me hard for like a full minute until I said, "Mom? I kind of can't breathe." I don't think she knew that I was lying to her about the notebook, but I'm pretty sure she knew I wasn't telling the truth.

After that, I was bigger than TV in our house, and that's saying a lot. Mom kept a close eye on me, and Dad was pretty interested in my moods and whereabouts as well. I was like the star of my own reality series, except for the fact that the only people watching were my mother and father. And I wasn't on just once a week; I was broadcasting every day, all day.

Dad came into my room one evening, sat on my bed, and asked if there was maybe something I wanted to discuss with him. I watched as little beads of sweat began to form on his brow. His leg twitched and though he tried to hold my gaze, his eyes kept shifting toward the door as though he was sizing up the exits in case of an emergency. I knew that Mom had put him up to this and I could tell that he wanted to go back downstairs and watch his show on TV. I took pity on him and said, "I'm good." He gave me a pat on the shoulder and told me that any time I needed to talk with him, mano-a-mano, he was available 24-7.

NINE

Meanwhile school continued to be dreaded and horrible. Whose idea was school anyway? A sadist's, no doubt. For example, my particular form of torture was being trapped in an environment in which everyone was going around saying that I was gay. Whether I am gay or not is not the issue. The issue is this: it is wrong to declare someone *else*'s sexuality, and it is equally wrong to go around demanding that someone declare his or her own sexuality if he or she doesn't feel like it. Just because you yourself happen to be uncomfortable with uncertainty and can't stand ambiguity and/or paradox, does not mean that everyone in the world is wired in the same way. Some of us prefer to remain a mystery—even to ourselves—until we are ready.

The GSA-ers were the worst; they claimed that I was in denial, and they told me to my face (repeatedly) that if I would just admit my homosexual tendencies I would feel a whole lot better about myself. I thought they were just trying to up their membership and make it seem as though the Gay-Straight-Alliance was a real club with actual members instead of a fringe group of geeks with dyed hair and pierced eyebrows. I told them (repeatedly) that I would feel a whole lot better if they would just leave me alone, which of course they didn't seem to want to do. They suggested that I consider labeling myself "Questioning" and leave it at that. Or maybe I could declare myself an "ally." I asked them why I needed a label at all; why did I need to declare myself as anything other than Trevor? Isn't that enough?

Miranda Lemley, a sophomore with a round face, sparkly blue eyes, baggy pants, perfunctory piercings, and an impressive grill of dental work, sighed hard. As she fussed with her green Mohawk, she said, "Look, Travis, we're just trying to be friendly. You seem lost and lonely. Once upon a time we were the same way, so we thought you could use a kind word. But if you're gonna be that way about it, forget we ever said anything." She then turned on her heel and walked away. The others followed after her.

"TREVOR," I called out after her. "My name is Trevor!"

The jocks also began to taunt and abuse me. Without Pinky and his posse around to provide a little street cred, I might as well have been wearing a target on my back. In addition to *Faggot*, some of the names they called me to my face were as follows: *Fruit Loop, Poof, Sissy, Girlyboy, Nellie,*

Big Nell-box, Nancy, Mary, and *Evelyn.* There was a large football player named Turk who apparently decided that his mission in life was to make my life extra miserable. Why Turk felt the need to pick on *me* when there happened to be so many other kids in our school who were weaker, more defenseless, and (excuse me for saying it) more deserving, remains a mystery to this day. In any case, Turk found it in his heart to jab me with his fist, his elbow, his knee, his thumb, a book, or whatever he had handy whenever I passed him in the hallway. And because he was the king of the jocks, his minions did the same. As a way of defending myself I tried to make myself invisible, but again and again I was unable to activate that particular superpower. At night, I busied myself by deleting the hateful comments that were posted to my Facebook wall. It was exhausting work, but the thought that Pinky might be checking out my profile and could possibly see these remarks made me work even harder and I was kept up late into the night.

Sometimes to entertain myself I tried to imagine the unhappy futures that were in store for my fellow schoolmates. For example, I envisioned Turk living in a one-bedroom, low-rise apartment with a partial view of an unremarkable third-tier American city. I imagined that by the age of 30 Turk would be stuck in a job that went nowhere and meant nothing. He would have neither a wife nor a girlfriend, maybe a cat. His football trophies would be placed prominently on top of his TV, but only he would admire them. Most nights he would sit there trying to figure out where he went wrong. How did it happen that one day he was so on top of the world and then practically overnight he was nothing, no one? Then one evening after months and months of soul-searching, it would come to him in a flash. *I see now,* he would say to himself. *I should've been nicer to that Trevor kid back in high school. Everything in my life would be different if I just hadn't been so outright mean to him.* Later that evening he would get the idea to call me so he could make it up to me personally, tell me that he was sorry before it was too late. He would look me up on Facebook, and when he couldn't find me there he'd go to the White Pages website and do a search. Sadly, he would not be able to find me there either because it would be too late. I'd already be dead.

TEN

I came home from my piano lesson and found Father Joe sitting on our living room sofa. He looked like a dark cloud in his priestly blacks and clerical collar, but a cloud with a big smile and a firm handshake. Right away, he offered to take me to the Dairy Queen. I was suspicious from the start. First of all, we were never that religious as a family. Yes, we believed in God, but we were never that big on His local representatives regardless of their affiliation. For example, I can't remember any one of them being invited into our house. Ever. Father Joe and I drove across town to the Dairy Queen in Father Joe's blue, midsize Malibu, and the whole time he asked me questions about my schoolwork, about how I was getting on with Mom and Dad, and about the kids at school.

Father Joe had a big doughy face with features that were unremarkable: nose, lips, eyes, and chin were all standard issue, not one of them stood out among the others. I noticed that his hands were unnaturally clean and he kept his fingernails neatly clipped. Dandruff dotted his shoulders like the first bit of snow on a paved street. And the whole time he was talking, I couldn't help wondering if he had ever kissed a girl. Did he turn against a life of sex and then decide to devote himself to God, or was it the other way around? Did he find God and then force himself to forgo the sex altogether? Either way, it seemed a shame. Not that I was interested in having sex with Father Joe. Please. But still, shouldn't everyone have the right to enjoy themselves in this world? Shouldn't everyone be loved? And why would God want a person to *not* have sex? What would be the point of that?

Anyway, he parked the Malibu around the side of the building, and as he ran down the list of ice cream treats we might enjoy, I found myself actually praying: *Please, God, do not let anyone from school see me in the company of a priest on a Saturday afternoon. No offense, but it will ruin me.*

Instead of accompanying Father Joe into the place, I opted to stay in the car and wait for him to bring me a hot-fudge sundae. And it's a good thing because, as I was going through the glove compartment (a Bible, a pack of tissues, a county map, a bottle of aspirin, the registration, and a book of matches from a bar called The Hideaway), I happened to look up and spot Miranda Lemley walking into the Dairy Queen with a few of her lesbian friends. I thanked God for saving me the embarrassment of being recognized, and promised to do charitable works for the rest of my life. Eventually, Father Joe returned to the car and, just as I was about to dig into my sundae, he introduced the topic of sex.

"What about it?" I inquired.

Father Joe seemed to be under the impression that I didn't know where babies came from or how they got made. Before I could correct this misperception, he launched into a description of the process, giving me a blow-by-blow account of what men and women get up to when they are naked with each other. It was only then that I began to realize this whole outing had been a miserable set-up between my parents and Father Joe.

"So then the man's penis becomes blood engorged," said Father Joe as he reached for his soft drink and took a sip. "He gets hard."

How was it possible that this was happening? Why hadn't I seen it coming? I felt like a total stooge.

"And then the man inserts his penis into the vagina of the woman, which is lubricated in its own natural juices."

I swear it was like gag city.

And then just when I was grossed out to the max and humiliated to the point of never wanting to have sex with a single living person for the rest of my totally sorry life, Father Joe turned to me and said: "Trevor, have you ever had desires? And I'm talking about sexual desires for another boy."

I decided that in fact this was not happening; it was a bad dream. It was a nightmare and I'd be waking up in my bed in just a moment. Wake up, I told to myself. Wake up! Wake up! I tried to scream, but I found that just like in a dream, I couldn't. WAKE UP!

"Be honest with me, Trevor. I can help you if you are honest."

I looked away, hoping that by removing Father Joe from my sight I might somehow make him disappear from the

face of the earth or at least from my vicinity; it didn't work. I was still trapped in a nightmare, and he kept talking, making it worse.

"Have you, for example, ever wanted to touch another boy . . . like . . . and I'm not suggesting anything here, but, like Pinky Faraday?"

After that I can't remember much of what was said. I completely blocked him out, and all of my powers of concentration were focused on devising a getaway plan. I briefly considered opening the car door, leaping from my seat, and throwing myself into the oncoming highway traffic, but every time I took hold of the door handle, something made me pause. Eventually, Father Joe stopped talking, drove me back home, and dropped me off, but not without first promising that we would do this again real soon. What I wanted to say was: *Just kill me now.*

"How was your visit with Father Joe?" Mom called out from the kitchen.

"Fine," I replied as I ran up the stairs and into my room.

After what they'd put me through, I felt entirely justified in not mentioning my plans. Mom and Dad did not need to know that the following day I was going to start a new life. That was my business. But just so that the plan would remain fresh in my mind, I sat down at my desk and wrote it all out longhand.

MY PLAN

Dye hair and eye lashes.

Change name, identity.

Change schools.

MapQuest Mexico.

Change religion.

ELEVEN

They say that when you die your whole life flashes before you, but what they don't tell you is that the very last day is the worst day of all and you'd rather not replay it. There are no statistics, but I'm guessing that the last day is the final straw, proof that your life was so not worth living.

The toilet in the master bathroom flushed—a sure sign in our house that the day had officially begun. Mom was up. I could hear her humming.

Mister T, our cat, was downstairs, wide awake and waiting to be released into the wilds of the backyard in order to begin his daily business of disturbing (and possibly killing) whatever wildlife he can sink his teeth into. Mister T is a real terrorist, but rather than targeting a particular population such as field mice or house wrens, he likes to spread his enmity all around to include everything and everyone in view. We humans are especially subject to his disapproval. Only my mother seems to be exempt from being clawed, chased, hissed at, scratched, and bitten on a regular basis. I suspect that Mister T considers Mom necessary for his survival. When it comes to the rest of us, he either hisses at us in order to get us to understand that we are sitting in his spot or takes a swipe to let us know who is boss.

I've read stories on the Internet about how cats are supposed to know when a person is close to death. Apparently household cats have extrasensory powers that tell them to sleep outside the door of the soon-to-be-deceased. Possible? Sure. But no one has been able to prove it. Personally, I think it's just an urban legend, the result of that weird aura cats give off like swamp gas. In any case, Mister T would not be the right cat to study in order to prove this premise, because on any given day of the week, he could care less whether I am dead or alive. Most mornings he just sits at the back door, occasionally licking his chops, cleaning his paws, and waiting for my mother to open the back door and let him loose upon another unsuspecting day. Like everybody else in the house, Mister T had no idea what I was planning for myself.

I figured that if I actually went through with my plan, I would be spared the torture of having to face another day (i.e., Turk and the kids in the cafeteria). I was counting on this whole charade being over and done with and hoping that some kind of eternal silence would descend like snow falling on Christmas morning. In other words, I was looking forward to being done with this world.

But . . .

What if death wasn't really the end of everything? I mean no one really knows for sure what happens after you die. I've read about the afterlife on the Internet. People who died and then came back to life always say how peaceful their dead bodies appeared to be while they themselves were floating up near the ceiling looking down on the whole deathbed scene. I was looking forward to that kind of peace. In fact, I couldn't wait. I imagined the dead quiet, the eternal peace, the ceiling, the floating, the end.

But what if I was forced to witness the whole unhappy course of events that followed on the heels of my death? Suppose I had to stand by and watch my mother discover my dead body lying on the bed? That would be awful, and I wasn't sure that I could handle it.

Imagine that I'm sprawled out on the bed, staring up at the ceiling, eyes wide open, but seeing nothing. This time instead of just pretending that I'm dead, like I used to do on occasion, I am actually and truly dead. Mom walks into the room, sees me lying there, and freezes.

When she realizes what's going on, she lets out an involuntary scream. But in order not to wake Dad, she quickly catches herself and covers her mouth with both hands. She shuts the door. All the color has drained from my face and my skin has a bluish tint, making me look more than a little ghoulish. The color has drained from Mom's face too, but she is still alive. She falls down onto the carpet and, while kneeling beside the bed, she takes hold of my shoulders, shakes me, and repeats the words, "Why, why, why?" over and over. My face is cold as stone but I look relaxed, peaceful, and almost happy. My plaid Converse high-tops are lying on the floor beside the bed, their mouths wide open and tongues hanging out. Mom picks up one of the sneakers, looks at it as if it is something that's fallen from outer space, and then she unexpectedly presses it to her heart. I am forced to watch her as she starts to sob uncontrollably. I don't say anything. I can't. I'm up near the ceiling, dead. And besides, what would I say? "It's going to be all right. Don't worry, Mom, I'll do better next time." No. I just have to float there and endure her heartache until the pain becomes too much and I am forced to fly off to God knows where.

This was the kind of thinking that could sometimes discourage me from going through with my plan. But then I would tell myself, "*It's a good thing that your mind is made up. Now all you need are the means to do it.*"

TWELVE

Most mornings while waiting for the school bus, I sit on the front stoop of our house and daydream. Because my present is usually too horrible to think about, I spend a lot of the time imagining various futures for myself, all of them fantastic and amazing.

I was someone leading an extreme and glamorous life somewhere in the tropics.

I was famous and everyone wanted to be photographed in my presence.

I had a three-picture deal with a major movie studio.

Lady Gaga and I were best friends; we were a team, touring the world together. I designed her outfits and pyrotechnical displays; she bought me a car.

The thought of these various career opportunities kept me very busy in my mind; they passed the time. But that spring, as my popularity diminished to the point that even I didn't

want to hang out with myself, I realized Mexico wasn't going to cut it and I began to imagine what it would be like if I died an early death.

I practiced for my funeral. For long stretches I would lie on my bed in my best and only suit. I lit candles and incense. I looked great, peaceful. And I imagined people coming up to my coffin, one by one and paying their last respects. Many of them cried. People I hardly knew said things like: *I should've seen it coming. We had no idea. I could've been nicer to him. Who knew that he was suffering? He was always such a cheerful child.* Anyway, the funeral thing just made me feel better about the whole situation, and I began to consider it as a real option.

I began to delete certain pictures of myself from my phone and from my computer. I wanted only the ones that I considered flattering to remain after I was gone. I organized my poems and made a file of the ones that I especially liked, the ones that best expressed my life journey. My play, *Nevermore the Wind*, which had been announced as part of the Spring Dramathon, was printed, copied, and bound. The dedication read: To anyone who has ever heard the wind.

I deleted the movie of Pinky that I had on my camera. It wasn't a secret. At the time, I told him I was recording it so that we could review it later and work on his dance steps, but he had already quit the show by the time I had it fully edited. In the movie, he looked so handsome, slightly sweaty, and totally into the task at hand. Sometimes as a form of personal torture I would sit in my room and view it over and over. Even though his dancing sucked and he had no stage presence, he was a bright beacon of hope up on that stage; he knew how to laugh at himself and that made people smile. To me, he represented all kinds of possibilities that I could not have articulated at the time. Still can't.

When you're young, people tell you that you'll get over stuff; they say it as though what you're feeling isn't really real or it's just practice for what comes later on in life. But what we have now is all that matters. The love we feel today is what we know of love; good or bad, it's what we've got to work with. People don't recognize that sometimes a feeling is so intense it makes you just want to lay down and die rather than go on feeling it. I'm not saying that that's a good thing; I'm just saying that it happens. And I know because it happened to me.

Anyway, I missed the bus that morning. I guess I was concentrating so hard on the future that I missed what was happening right then and there. Both Zac and Katie saw me running after the bus, but rather than make the driver stop for me, they just laughed at me as they drove off.

I was late for school and had to go to the office. Usually Mrs. Rodriguez gives you a note and then she makes some kind of mark under your name in The Book of Lateness. Also all first-period teachers have perfected a scowl suitable for latecomers, but that's about all that happens. No big deal. Life goes on. But that day, Mrs. Rodriguez came out from behind her barricade and told me that Principal Davis wanted to see me right away in her office.

"I'm so sorry about all this, Trevor," Principal Davis said as soon as she hung up the phone. "I really am. And we are doing everything we can to get to the bottom of it and find out who is responsible."

I felt a little crazy because I had no idea what she was talking about, and the more she kept on assuring me that everything was going to be all right, the more I was starting to freak. I felt like I was in that Franz Kafka short story, the one we read in English class about the guy who wakes up and discovers he's been changed into a bug, but doesn't realize it until it's too late.

"Do *you* know anything about how this might've happened?" she asked me.

I did not. And by that point I was so alarmed by what *it* might turn out to be that I just shook my head and left it at that.

"Would you like to call your parents?"

Again, I shook my head, this time more vigorously.

Mom and Dad have told me again and again that I am not to call them at work unless it is a real emergency. And since I didn't know the nature of the problem, I technically couldn't consider it as such. And what's more, I really didn't want to know.

"I have to go home," I told Principal Davis.

"Of course, of course," she replied, nodding her head and giving me a look of serious concern. "Shall I have someone drive you?"

"No, thanks. The walk will be good for me. The fresh air and all."

My plan was to make a quick stop at my locker, ditch my gym clothes and pick up a few things that I might need just in case I never came back to school. The hallways were deserted and I could almost feel the walls and floors breathing a sigh of relief. In about five minutes the place would be heaving with the jostle of a thousand teenagers, each of whom had very specific fears and hopes and loves and disappointments; it was a volatile mix and I was happy to be relieved of it, even if it was just for one day. I was sure that the cause for Principal Davis's concern would be revealed soon enough, and that I wasn't going to like it. In any case, it could wait.

As I turned the corner, I could see Mr. Hooper at the far end of the hallway, standing by my locker with his back to me. He was wearing his usual janitor uniform: khaki shirt with his name embroidered in script above the pocket, khaki pants with keys dangling from his belt, dust-colored work boots, and a wool hat featuring our school colors and team mascot. As I got closer I could see the collection of paint cans, rags, and brushes that he had lined up on the floor beside him. He was so into his work that he didn't notice my approach. In fact, I stood right beside him for what seemed like about a year. I had plenty of time to read, over and over, the letters that had been deliberately scratched into my locker.

F.

A.

G.

G.

O.

T.

"Oh," said Mr. Hooper, startled by my presence. "This your locker, huh?"

At that moment, the bell rang, doors flew open, and the hall began to fill with the teaming masses. All I knew was that I had to get out of there before anyone saw me. I took off down the hall, my eyes fixed on the emergency exit door and the world beyond.

THIRTEEN

Dear Mom and Dad,

I don't want you to think I haven't given this a lot of thought, because I have. I tried to cure myself, but nothing worked. Don't think it's your fault. It's not. It just happens. I'm different and there is nothing in this world that's going to make that change. Please give all my Lady Gaga DVDs and posters to Katie Quinn who happens to love Lady G. as much as I do. And please, if it's possible, play "Born This Way" at my funeral. It says everything. It's the title song from her second album and it's my absolute fave. And don't cry too much. It would've been a skillion times worse if I had lived.

Your loving son,
Trevor

FOURTEEN

FIFTEEN

The people at the hospital informed me that a person cannot commit suicide by taking too many aspirin. But they pretty much guaranteed me that I wouldn't have a headache for like another year.

I think they were kidding.

Mom and Dad were by my bedside when I woke up, and I could tell by the state of their faces that they'd been crying. They kept saying how sorry they were for everything. And even though I kept assuring them that it wasn't their fault, they couldn't take it in. They seemed very determined to make up for it somehow or at least to make it right. It was kind of sweet to watch them in action. Dad canceled all his business trips for the next month. He said that he was going to stay home and teach me to play football.

"Really, Dad," I told him. "Go to work. I hate football. Seriously."

"Well, then, something," he said, looking at me with the saddest set of eyes I've ever seen on a man.

Mom kept blaming herself for missing the cues. She said things like, "I should've known." Or "Why didn't I see it coming?" I tried to comfort her by reminding her that she had a lot on her plate. She told me, "That's no excuse. You're my kid, and I'm going to do better from now on. And we're going to see a therapist. Together. All three of us."

Great. Football and therapy.

Suicide turned out to be not the greatest idea in terms of my future options. I was suddenly looking at a life in which I was trapped, grounded, and suspect. But I guess it was way better than the life of quiet desperation that I'd been quietly and desperately living. We are all in it together now. And of course I am alive.

Zac came walking into my hospital room with eyes downcast and hands clasped together in altar boy fashion. He looked like a guy who was being forced to view the open coffin at his best friend's funeral—not crying, but wanting to. The minute he looked up and saw me lying in the hospital bed, he broke down sobbing into my bed sheet. He said that if I ever tried anything like that again he'd kill me with his bare hands. Then he insisted that I give him the names of every kid in school who was ever mean to me because he was going to totally kick their asses.

Sweet.

Fortunately Katie had gone to visit her aunt and she wasn't expected back until after the weekend. We all agreed that it would be better if she didn't know about "my little episode" (as Mom called it). If Katie found out that she had missed an opportunity to save my life or nurse me back to health, she'd be bitterly disappointed. And also Katie didn't really understand the concept of keeping a secret. I mean she understood that a secret is confidential; it's just that the number of people in whom she had confidence was very large. The news would have spread throughout the school and for the remainder of my high school years I'd be a famous head case—a situation I could definitely do without.

Thankfully, my stay at the hospital was brief. But while I was there I had an opportunity to meet a nurse named Jack. Jack was super nice. Actually, Jack was a candy striper, which is almost like a nurse, only younger. Jack was full of all kinds of interesting information. For example, he told me that he believed people who committed suicide just had to come back and live a whole lifetime all over again.

"Good to know," I told him, as he plumped my pillow. "Because the thought of growing up again with my parents makes me totally depressed. Once around the block with them is plenty."

He laughed and said that it didn't work that way. "You wouldn't necessarily come back into the same family and all."

"Right," I replied. "But knowing my luck, I would."

He gave me some advice, which I didn't mind taking because once upon a time he himself had been through something just like I had. He suggested that I might want to find someone I can talk on a regular basis about my problems.

"Y'mean, like a shrink?" I asked, thinking that maybe he considered me a lunatic.

"Or like a friend," he replied. "Someone you can trust." When he said that, the gravity of the situation hit me. What if I'd actually died? When I thought about how I might have never met Jack, or how sad my parents would've been without me, or how Zac and Katie might have lost a friend forever, I turned my face to the wall and started to cry. Jack didn't seem surprised, he even had a tissue box handy.

"What do I do now?" I asked him between sobs. He lightly touched my shoulder and then quietly reminded me that I didn't have to *do* anything today other than breathe. He said that starting tomorrow I might want to consider living my life one day at a time. No big decisions. Just for a while. Stay in the moment. As much as I can. Appreciate what's right in front of me. I looked at him and told him that I'd give it a try.

He made me promise that I would never do anything like kill myself, and if I ever thought about doing harm to myself I was to call him right away. He scribbled his cell phone number on the back of the tissue box and handed it to me.

"*I promise*," I thought, clutching the box to me. I didn't say it out loud, but maybe it wasn't necessary. Jack looked to me like a friend, someone I would be able to trust someday, someone I might call.

The next day, just as I was leaving the hospital with Mom and Dad, Zac showed up and stopped us in the hallway. His eyes were wild with excitement, the way they get when he discovers a new constellation through the lens of his high-powered telescope, like he's taken in too much light.

Anyway, he wanted to know what I was doing on Saturday. I thought he was going to give me information about some totally deadbeat support group for gay, suicidal teenagers, so I told him that I was all set.

"Oh," he replied.

But then he pulled out what looked like two tickets from his pocket and added: "'Cause yours truly scored two tickets to the Lady Gaga concert Saturday night. I thought, well . . . if it's okay with your parents, it might be fun for you and me to go. Whatd'ya think?"

Mom and Dad looked at one another and then agreed that it was my call as long as I felt up to it. Okay, so maybe it was just the tickets, but right then and there I made a decision—I was going to live.

At least until Saturday.

AFTERWORD

At the start of my sophomore year of high school I was assigned to Mr. Shust's English class. He was a cranky and fastidious man of middle years who dressed in tweeds and flannel and insisted that his students keep a journal. He told us that the experience would enrich our lives (whatever that meant) and we would be graded not on the quality of our writing, but on our willingness to participate. So every evening after my homework was finished, I dutifully made an entry into the black-and-white speckled composition book. I began by chronicling the minor and major moments of my life, the hurts, hopes, and heartbreaks, and after a while writing became a habit. When I entered my twenties, I had a shelf filled with a written record of my adolescent years. These notebooks certainly came in handy years later, when I began the difficult work of becoming a writer.

One morning, while sitting at my desk and sipping coffee, I heard a news report about teen suicide on the radio. According to statistics then, a young person who identified as gay or lesbian was three to four times more likely to attempt suicide than his or her heterosexual peers, and 33% of all teen suicides involved homosexual kids. I was appalled by this fact, and shocked that nothing was being done to prevent the loss of what I considered our greatest natural resource—our youth. Instinctively, I turned to my old journals and I began to read. For the first time in years, I was reminded of just how confusing it was for me as an adolescent—how painful and lonely. There on those pages was my story. I immediately wrote the first few lines of a story about a thirteen-year-old boy who confides to his journal. I called him Trevor.

Dear Diary,
Tonight I walked into the living room while Mom and Dad were watching TV. Fell dead to the floor. No response from them. I think that television reruns have replaced their natural spontaneity. I mean, unless I'm on the eleven o'clock news, I don't think they'd care. And even then they might sleep through it.

Eventually Trevor discovers that he is different—different from his parents, different from his schoolmates, and different from his best friend. *Trevor* is a poignant and humorous portrait of a boy in crisis, but it's also about anyone who has ever felt as though they just can't get it right and they don't fit in no matter how hard they try.

It wasn't that difficult to find the inspiration for Trevor. All of us have felt this way at one time or another, especially during our teenage years when we are just beginning to piece together the story of ourselves. Fortunately, my story was close at hand and my journals were stuffed with poems, rants, dreams, prayers, vows, ideas, and remembrances of what it meant to be fourteen, fifteen, sixteen . . . The irony was that just as I was beginning to discover myself, I was becoming a stranger to the people I loved the most—my family. I felt that they couldn't know me, not *really*, because if they knew who I was they would most certainly reject me. I couldn't live with that—not even as a possibility. And so I kept myself a secret from them, moved further and further away from them, and began to explore life and love without them.

I went on to perform *Trevor* onstage as part of my solo show, *Word of Mouth*, and eventually the show found its way to the HBO Comedy Festival in Aspen and then Off-Broadway where, incredibly, I won the prestigious New York Drama Desk Award for best solo performance of that year. One night following a performance of *Word of Mouth*,

I met Randy Stone and Peggy Rajsk, and they asked me to consider writing the screenplay for a short film based on the story of *Trevor*.

The resulting 18-minute film (produced by Randy Stone and directed and produced by Peggy Rajski) went on to win many awards, including an Academy Award for Best Live Action Short. It was an exciting time as we watched our little film find an audience and spread the word that gay was okay—and during a period when LGBT issues were just beginning to find their way into the news. The times were changing and *Trevor* was in some small way able to contribute to that change. In 1997 when we sold the film to HBO, we thought it might be a good idea to flash a telephone number at the end in case there happened to be a kid out there who could relate to the character of Trevor and needed someone to talk to. We wanted to let young people know that it was all right to reach out and ask for help. Someone would always be standing by to listen to their problems. But after doing some research we found that there was no national 24-hour crisis intervention and suicide prevention lifeline for gay teens. And so we set out to create one.

Three months later, The Trevor Project was launched, and finally lesbian, gay, bisexual, transgender, and questioning teens had a place to turn. That first night we received over 1,500 calls, and we've been at it ever since. Every year we receive approximately 30,000 calls from young people around the country. Of course, not every call requires a rescue and not all of the young people identify as LGBT, but every call comes from someone who is struggling with issues of identity and is a person between the ages of 13 and 24 who is in need of someone who will listen. Thrown out of their homes, shunned by friends, often with no one to whom they can turn, these young people have found the help they need simply by calling 1-800-4-U-Trevor.

These days, young adult novels are full of complex lesbian and gay characters. Twenty-first century authors like David Levithan, Alex Sanchez, Jacqueline Woodson, Bill Konigsberg, and Mayra Lazara Dole write eloquently and often about the issues affecting the lives of LGBT teens. In fact, while perusing recent YA publishing lists of any major house, one might get the idea that it's not such a bad time to be a teen who is LGBT-identified. But amazingly and alarmingly, the statistics today remain no better than they were over twenty years ago when I first sat down to write *Trevor*. LGBT youth are still killing themselves and statistics indicate that they are four times more likely to attempt suicide than their heterosexual peers. Fortunately, The Trevor Project continues to provide every young person with a place they can go to receive the encouragement they need to live fully and with hope, and, most importantly, the support they need to keep on living life.

Recently Dan Savage's very successful "It Gets Better" campaign created a viral revolution and allowed adults to send out a message loud and clear to youth that life would indeed get better, if only they could hang on a bit longer. It also helped The Trevor Project become the go-to organization for youth who are struggling with their sexuality and identity. As a result, our call volume has spiked. We opened a third call center, which is located in Harvey Milk's old camera shop in San Francisco, and which is dedicated to Harvey's memory. We've also taken a much more active role in communicating to youth that we are here for them 24/7. In addition to the lifeline, we've designed outreach and educational programs. We launched TrevorSpace last year, a secure online destination where youth can connect with one another, offer one another peer-to-peer support, and share information, and less than a year later we have close to 20,000 registered and active members. Another feature we have developed is *Ask Trevor*, through which young people can write in and ask questions that are not time sensitive, and read our responses online. We have launched *Trevor Chat*, an online destination where teens can chat with a trained counselor and get some guidance *before* a crisis occurs. We have also been instrumental in introducing anti-bullying legislation on the state and federal level. We even have an in-school program where we train educators and students, meeting youth, on their home turf and talking to them about the power of words and the value of listening.

Despite all these new developments and online services, we remain first and foremost a lifeline, offering voice-to-voice communication, saving lives, and working to normalize help-seeking behavior. In a world that is becoming increasingly depersonalized because of digital media, we remain dedicated to providing every young person, regardless of his or her identity, the opportunity to be heard—and they needn't wait until a crisis occurs to call on us. If I had understood at fourteen that asking for help is an essential part of the human experience, I might have been able to get the help I needed sooner rather than later.

Of course, there is still much to do for youth everywhere. The passing of the Marriage Equality Act in New York State was a great win for youth who believe in the power of love, but the love of a teen in Texas is not yet equal to one living in New York, Connecticut, Iowa, Massachusetts, New Hampshire, Vermont, or Washington, DC. And further afield, homosexuality is illegal in more than 30 African nations, and in some places is a crime punishable by death. In some Islamic countries like Iran, Saudi Arabia, Sudan, and Yemen, homosexuals face imprisonment, corporal punishment, or in some cases, execution. The globe has shrunk to the size of the worldwide web and every young person has access it. They get the message, they hear the news, and we are working hard to incorporate their experiences into the stories they see and hear. Martin Luther King, Jr. once said: "A threat to justice anywhere is a threat to justice everywhere," and his wisdom has perhaps never been better applied than to the struggle to make one person's love equal to everybody else's—regardless of gender, race, or sexual orientation.

Changing the story of LGBT and Questioning youth throughout the world and giving them the right to love is one way to ensure a better and more loving future for everyone. Young people, all of them, belong to our future, and without them we cannot realize tomorrow. Convincing even one kid that his or her life is worth living is to convince ourselves that the world itself is worth saving. I believe that all young people need to find stories they can believe in, stories that will bring them closer to understanding that they are perfect exactly as they are. I hope Trevor's story can be just that for generations to come.

Enjoy!

James
September 2011

ACKNOWLEDGMENTS

I t would be easy to say that the story of *Trevor* has had a life of its own, starting as it did as part of a theater piece in a small East Village theater and then moving further out and into the world until it inspired the founding of the The Trevor Project. But the truth is so many have made this story happen and I'd like to acknowledge some of them here.

I want to thank all those amazing people of the theater who helped me develop *Trevor* by providing me with a stage: Randy Rollison at HERE Arts Center in New York, Mitchell Riggs at Camilla's, and the legendary Ellen Stewart at La Mama Etc.; Eve Ensler for her profound devotion to the work, for teaching me what theater is capable of, and for being my sister; Julian Schlossberg, Elaine May, and Mike Nichols for their incredible support and for providing me with a wider audience; and Cy O'Neal for always believing in me and championing my cause.

I want to thank Randy Stone and Peggy Rajski for having the vision that the little story of *Trevor* could become a film. Their dedication and hard work allowed me to believe that there is no dream too big. Blessings to Jodie Foster for her generosity with the start-up funds to make the film. And my heartfelt thanks to Diane Wade who was there at the very beginning to make it all happen, and who continues to support The Trevor Project with her untiring efforts.

I am so grateful to Brett Barsky for bringing the character of Trevor so beautifully to life, and to his mom, Cheryl Astroff. Without Cheryl's courageous and generous heart, her thirteen-year-old son would never have found his way to us.

I want to thank HBO and Ellen Degeneres for their support of the film and for helping us get into the homes of a whole generation of LGBT and Questioning teens and at a time when the word "gay" was only just beginning to be spoken on TV.

I want to thank my amazing agent and friend, Bill Clegg, for always respecting me and fighting for me—and for coming up with the brilliant idea of turning the story of *Trevor* into a book for a new generation of LGBT and Questioning teens. Dan Simon and Crystal Yakacki at Seven Stories Press, for realizing this idea so perfectly and with such care.

Thank you to my wild tribe of brothers and sisters;

these are the people who encourage me with their lives and through their work: Amy Bloom, Melanie Braverman, Matt Burgess, Dustin Lance Black, David Cafiero, Kate Clinton, Ken Corbett, Michael Cunningham, Jimmy Davis, Stacey D'Erasmo, Michael Downing, Tom Duane, Joy Episalla, Chris Garneau, Meg Giles, Brad Goreski, Tim Hailand, David Hopson, Jim Hodges, Gary Janetti, Daniel Kaizer, Michael Klein, Mark Matousek, Armistead Maupin, Christian McCulloch, Ian McKellen, Hilla Medalia, Marty Moran, Adam Moss, Christopher Potter, Beth Povinelli, Dave Purcell, Mollie Purdue, Seth Pybas, Sal Randolph, Randy Redd, Duncan Sheik, Christopher Turner, Lorraine Whittington, and Carrie Yamaoka.

A special thanks to Sally Fisher and Jim Rogers of the Colin Higgins Foundation who provided us with the start-up money to begin The Trevor Project back in 1998 and who have stood by us ever since.

And my deepest gratitude to every lifeline counselor who ever answered a call from a kid in crisis; they are the true heroes of this story.

RESOURCE GUIDE

NATIONAL ORGANIZATIONS

Gay & Lesbian Alliance
Against Defamation (GLAAD)
5455 Wilshire Boulevard
Los Angeles, CA 90036
http://www.glaad.org/

GSA Network
1550 Bryant Street, #800
San Francisco, CA 94103
http://gsanetwork.org/

Gay and Lesbian Medical Association (GLMA)
1326 18th Street, NW, Suite 22
Washington, DC 20036
http://www.glma.org/

Human Rights Campaign (HRC)
1640 Rhode Island Avenue NW
Washington, DC 20036
http://www.hrc.org/

National Center for Transgender Equality
1325 Massachusetts Avenue, NW, #700
Washington, DC 20005
http://transequality.org/

Parents, Families and Friends of Lesbians and Gays (PFLAG)
1828 L Street NW, #660
Washington, DC 20036
www.pflag.org/

The Trevor Project
8704 Santa Monica Boulevard, Suite 200
West Hollywood, CA 90069
http://www.thetrevorproject.org/

TransYouth Family Allies (TYFA)
PO Box 1471
Holland, MI 49422
http://imatyfa.org/

American Civil Liberties Union (ACLU)
125 Broad Street, 18th Floor
New York, NY 10004
http://www.aclu.org/

Gay, Lesbian & Straight Education Network (GLSEN)
90 Broad Street
New York, NY 10004
www.glsen.org/

Lambda Legal
120 Wall Street, 19th Floor
New York, NY 10005
www.lambdalegal.org/

National Gay and Lesbian Taskforce (NGLTF)
1325 Massachusetts Avenue, NW, #600
Washington, DC 20005
http://thetaskforce.org/

WEBSITES

Advocates for Youth
www.advocatesforyouth.org

Amplify
www.amplifyyourvoice.org/youthresource

GLBT Near Me
www.glbtnearme.com

Go Ask Alice
www.goaskalice.columbia.edu

It Gets Better
http://www.itgetsbetter.org/

Lesbian, Gay, Bisexual and Transgender Health, CDC
www.cdc.gov/lgbthealth

Scarleteen
www.scarleteen.com

TrevorSpace
www.trevorspace.org

CRISIS INTERVENTION & SUICIDE PREVENTION LIFELINES

The Trevor Lifeline
866-4-U-Trevor (866-488-7386)

National Suicide Prevention Lifeline
800-273-TALK (8255)

THE TREVOR PROJECT

Each one of us deserves a chance to dream of the future, no matter who we love or how we express our gender. The Trevor Project is here for young lesbian, gay, bisexual, transgender, queer, and questioning people to help whenever you or a friend might need to talk to someone. Through our lifesaving programs and information, we work every day to help make the future better for all LGBTQ youth.

The Trevor Project operates the 24-hour Trevor Lifeline, and also the TrevorChat online messaging service, both connecting young LGBTQ people to open and accepting counselors, free of charge. Plus, there is TrevorSpace.org, where thousands of young LGBTQ people from all over the world can connect in a safe and accepting social space. Trevor is also on Facebook, Twitter, and YouTube, connecting young people with positive messages every day.

If you or someone you care about feels depressed or is

considering taking their own life, please call The Trevor Lifeline at: 866-488-7386. The call is free and confidential. Visit TheTrevorProject.org to learn more.

ABOUT THE AUTHOR

JAMES LECESNE wrote the Academy Award–winning short film *Trevor*, which inspired the founding of The Trevor Project. He produced the documentary film *After the Storm*, which chronicles the struggles of a group of teens in New Orleans in the aftermath of Hurricane Katrina, and he founded the After the Storm Foundation. He has published two young adult novels, *Absolute Brightness* and *Virgin Territory*. An actor as well as a writer, James has appeared on TV, in film, and in the theater. His solo show *Word of Mouth* was awarded both a NY Drama Desk Award and an Outer Critics Circle Award, and his play, *The Road Home: Stories of the Children of War*, was presented at the International Peace Conference at The Hague.

ABOUT SEVEN STORIES PRESS

Seven Stories Press is an independent book publisher based in New York City. We publish works of the imagination by such writers as Nelson Algren, Russell Banks, Octavia E. Butler, Ani DiFranco, Assia Djebar, Ariel Dorfman, Coco Fusco, Barry Gifford, Hwang Sok-yong, Lee Stringer, and Kurt Vonnegut, to name a few, together with political titles by voices of conscience, including the Boston Women's Health Collective, Noam Chomsky, Angela Y. Davis, Human Rights Watch, Derrick Jensen, Ralph Nader, Loretta Napoleoni, Gary Null, Project Censored, Barbara Seaman, Alice Walker, Gary Webb, and Howard Zinn, among many others. Seven Stories Press believes publishers have a special responsibility to defend free speech and human rights, and to celebrate the gifts of the human imagination, wherever we can. For additional information, visit www.sevenstories.com.